Latinas in
CORPORATE

Overcoming Cultural Obstacles
While Juggling a Career and a Family

MYRIAM DEL ANGEL

Latinas in CORPORATE

For more information visit:
Fig Factor Media, LLC | www.figfactormedia.com

Cover Design by DG Marco Alvarez
Layout by LDG Juan Manuel Serna Rosales

Printed in the United States of America

ISBN: 978-1-959989-15-8
Library of Congress Control Number: 2023905505

This book is dedicated to all the Latinas who are not only surviving the corporate world but THRIVING in it!

TABLE OF CONTENTS

ACKNOWLEDGEMENTS

"Fear is inevitable, I have to accept that, but I cannot allow it to paralyze me." —Isabel Allende

———————

I would like to thank my parents, **Myriam Sofia Acosta** and **Francisco Carlos Del Angel (RIP)**, for instilling in me the value of perseverance. I come from a very proud Colombian and Mexican household where my parents were both entrepreneurs, my mother owned a beauty salon, and my father was a mechanic. They worked very hard and seeing them grow and succeed despite their limited English and education taught me that you could achieve anything. *¡Muy bendecida!*

To my sisters from other misters who have brought joy, friendship, and support into my life: **Monica Briseno,** who is always willing to help me in whatever I need and encourages me, always saying, "You got this!" **Sarah Inciong** has helped me through a big transition in my life and provided me with guidance, resources, and tools, and **Beatriz Sahagun,** whom I have known since kindergarten and who has always had my back! She keeps me grounded and has the biggest heart I know. *¡Las quiero, hermanas!*

Thank you to my **Latinas Rising Up in Human Resources book sisters.** You have shown me what it is like to be in a sisterhood, and I am grateful to be surrounded by strong women who have demonstrated sacrifice, resilience, and strength. *¡Mi familia!*

Many thanks to the ladies who took the time to speak with me and share their stories. I'm honored to have you all as part of my circle of strong women. *¡Mil gracias!*

I want to express my gratitude to **Priscilla Guasso** for believing in me, giving me a voice, and giving me the confidence to go after my aspirations and goals. I admire all that you do and how you support the advancement and success of other women. *¡Te aprecio!*

For providing me with the direction and encouragement to establish a forum for me to tell a story, I am grateful to **Jackie Camacho-Ruiz and the Fig Factor Team.** I am incredibly appreciative to be a member of your book community! *¡Mi comunidad!*

To my ex-husband, **Domingo Miranda, Jr.**, thank you for the laughter and memories we shared, as well as for listening to all my corporate challenges and supporting me as best you could. *¡Buenos tiempos!*

Finally, I would like to thank my amazing children, **Laila, Mia, and Luca**. They are genuine, thoughtful, beautiful human beings and have been such an inspiration in my life. I love them wholeheartedly and am so blessed to be their mom. *¡Mi vida!*

FOREWORD
By Priscilla Guasso

Hoping for change is not enough.

It was a Saturday morning; the sun was beaming into my apartment building as I caught up with Myriam over the phone. She shared this idea and calling to write a book that anonymously would share different perspectives of executive Latinas in the corporate world. I leaned in and was intrigued to learn more.

Myriam and I met two years ago as I launched and founded what is now *Latinas Rising Up In HR*. From the first day we had dinner, she was upfront, energetic, and honest with who she was, what she had dreams for, and why she wanted to join our movement. She shared how much she loved her kids and was ready to do something to help change the course of Latino leadership.

Years later, I am not surprised at the launch of this book as she captivates amazing connections and is a serial networker looking to build bridges to lift others in our community. As much as I share how much I love meeting new people, Myriam is one of my favorite people to go to events with, and I love when I meet new folks in different cities, and they say, "I know of you... I met Myriam, one of your contributing authors!"

As one moves up in leadership, we learn more and more that we are far from perfect, and what makes the most impact is our vulnerability, our follow through, and our heart to serve—that is what I admire most about the people I surround myself with and see in Myriam.

She is the first to reach out and share the good, bad, and ugly with you. We have grown as professionals in the HR space. Combining my seventeen-plus years and her twenty-plus years of experience has led us to many thought-provoking conversations about how much the corporate world needs to change, why the strategic moves in our careers were made, and the lessons we learned from our own mistakes and those around us.

As you'll read in this book, no career is linear. When you layer that with your personal desires (marriage, divorce, family, IVF, adoption), world events (pandemic, recession, layoffs, etc.), and leadership that doesn't get it...Moving into executive leadership requires constant perseverance, confidence, tenacity, grit, and community.

One of the qualities I admire most about Myriam's leadership is her passion for supporting others in their careers. She's the first to help you with a career call, represent on a panel, participate as a mentor, and lead a dialogue. She has been a pioneer in HR, constantly pushing the needle by working remotely and leaning into all facets of HR. She doesn't shy away from hard conversations. I am eternally grateful to have her in my close community of confidants holding you accountable and pushing you to be even greater than you may see yourself.

In October of 2022, I had the pleasure of having Myriam work by my side on building the content for our inaugural conference to ensure we were hitting the mark for our community.

She was laser-focused on working with me to ensure our content was educational and would bring all attendees to the next level in their mindsets and careers.

When we first spoke over dinner of her thoughts and desires for this book, it was clear to me through that shimmer that came from her eyes that she found how she could leverage her voice to support others. Like many of us in HR, the past few years have been extremely difficult as we had over 98% of HR professionals say they were completely BURNT OUT. Some of my favorite conversations were about how we disrupt the business, HR, and DEI alike. Storytelling continues to be essential, and I am confident that what you'll read in this book is not just phenomenal research, but emotion bridged with an intellectual call to action.

It is an honor for me to be forever a part of this book being published. I hope it continues to be a vessel of education for us all and a tool for your toolbox to elevate more Latinas across all industries in the corporate world. As you read from the statistics, our community, with the support of great allies, is striving with a great passion for changing the paradigm of what leadership is today. We must do so boldly by embracing all of who we are with organizations that value our whole selves. As great as this sounds, there are many experiences that go untold and are lost as we're all trying to figure them out.

Reading through the next few chapters, I invite you to walk into the shoes of these powerful executives knowing these are true stories. As I've interviewed quite a few Latinas myself, I continue to pause in admiration that even though the current climate isn't always welcoming of us, there are still so many outstanding leaders inside and outside our community helping pave the way. It is through leaders like Myriam that are using their talents to create a domino effect that will continue to push us forward through change.

These experiences you'll read do not define our community but serve as an education to know that the good, bad, and ugly to rise to the top of leadership is extremely difficult and, at times, feels draining, impossible, and unattainable. As you continue through the next chapters, these are just a few examples that demonstrate why there is a lack of Latina representation and shows why.

I recently spoke with a close Latina executive regarding a Latino/Latina executive roundtable she attended. In disbelief, she said, "Priscilla, I can't believe we're still discussing the same thing twenty years later. We barely move .5% of representation in the c-suite and executive levels. When does this story end, and a new one gets told?"

I wish I had a magic wand to answer this. This story remains the same until we come together as ONE community, truly supporting each other in our celebratory moments, providing feedback to help elevate the game for each other, and being there when we break or are made to feel broken.

As you read these chapters of raw truths of women that shared intimate experiences as they climbed up the ladder as current executives, I invite you to lean into the emotion you experience when reading and think, what would I do? Moving forward, how can I be part of the solution? Find ways to get involved, speak up, join a movement, be active in your organizations... mentor and sponsor other Latinas.

In two years, through the help of Myriam and many other amazing women like her, I have seen the power of rolling up your sleeves, leaving your title at the door, and being a part of a difference that is 100% possible. It takes work, requires more than intention, and that you put your focus on action. Use your skills as Myriam has here and find what your space is to make a difference. Our kids, the future of this country, must see leadership modeled by our community not just on social media... but in our own households.

I get it; you might be thinking, "Priscilla, this sounds great, but I don't have time. I'm exhausted and feel like I can't do anything more than keep my head above water some days." I then ask of you... the day you are crossed with an opportunity to lift someone, open a door, speak positivity to promote another Latina and truly act on this... do it. You have so many organizations around you doing phenomenal work, and you may be that missing puzzle piece to help them get to the next level in making a difference. Many of our executives are balancing so many moving pieces. But as Myriam strives to educate us all here with many experiences, we hope that we as a collective community can make greater strides and that achieving it won't take another twenty years.

In many of the conversations I have had with Latinas at

different organizations, I hear an ongoing comment/theme. I don't trust that my leader will take this feedback the right way; there is a lack of trust; I don't want this to become larger than what it is; what is the missing gap, I'm passed over, even if I say something they're just going to take it personally and it will ruin my career trajectory.

If only I could count the number of LinkedIn messages, I get about having a quick coffee to vent and brainstorm on how to approach leadership perpetuating a culture contrary to inclusion and valuing our diversity. It is one of the main reasons I immediately said yes to supporting Myriam's idea to bring this project to life.

This book is coming at such a convenient time because these stories need to be brought to light. As corporate America leans into diversity and inclusion, it requires us to walk through the muddy waters of reality happening within the organization, facing head-on that your representation within the company doesn't tell a good story today but that your long-term investment in changing policies, conducting focused listening tours, conducting 360's, investing in coaching opportunities, and elevating our community to the next level will take time, but needs to remain consistent.

It requires leadership at all levels to get comfortable with getting uncomfortable so that moments of growth and learning can come about. It's well-known that people do not leave companies; they leave their leaders. Let that sink in for a second. While this book is a great read for all Latina leaders, I also invite our community to give these books to non-Latino executive leaders. It's a safe and educational way to share true experiences with your executive team and discuss how your team will combat this in your organization. When was the last time your team brought your Latino talent together to hear THEIR voices, experiences, and career aspirations directly? And what comes next is just as important: What will you do about it?

In a recent article, I read a phenomenal quote from Michelle Obama where she shares, "Success isn't about how much money you make; it's about the difference you make in people's lives." As leaders of people, take on that responsibility to your core and remember that you have all the power and ability to ensure your organization's culture pivots by how you lead through your actions. In a world where there are so many competing priorities, and your leaders are still learning what it means and takes to "get to the top," ask yourself: whose career in the Latino community are you supporting so that they get to your career success in half the time it took you?

We each have keys of connection, success, and knowledge to leave to others with a responsibility to share it in each of our interactions. Through Myriam's vision, this book clearly demonstrates what our executives are persevering to get to the top.

Thank you, Myriam, for the opportunity to be a part of this shift you're looking to make for Latinas in the corporate world, and for bringing a voice to what is truly happening to several of our executives that look to use their experiences to lift others. I hope this book continues to be the fire that will light our future path as we look for new disruptive and inclusive ways to change the face of leadership that represents the diversity within our Latino community for years to come.

Priscilla Guasso
Author, Founder & Speaker
Latinas Rising Up in HR®

INTRODUCTION

Before we begin, let me define the term I will use to identify who we are. There are currently four words in use. We are described as Hispanic (people, cultures, or countries associated with Spain, the Spanish language, or Hispanidad), Latino/a (Anyone born in or with ancestors from Latin America who is currently living in the United States, including Brazilians), Latinx (in place of gendered terms such as Latino or Latina, a gender-neutral term for members of the Latin American or Hispanic communities), and Latine (created by LGBTQIA+ Spanish speakers, makes use of the letter "e" to demonstrate gender inclusivity). Language evolves in tandem with the terminology we use to describe ourselves. While your self-identification should be based on your personal choices, there are no absolute standards for deciding what phrases are best for others. In my book, I choose to use Latina or Latino.

What does it take to be a successful Latina professional? Because success can mean different things to different people, this question may have multiple answers. Anyone who knows me will tell you two things: one, I'm passionate about helping other women, and two, I enjoy networking, meeting new people, and hearing their stories. During my twenty-plus years in the corporate world, I've met many Latinas who struggle with what success means to them daily. This is a question I also ask myself as I balance my job, family, and my me time.

Growing up in a traditional Latino household, success meant having a roof over our heads, food on the table, a family, and the ability to take one vacation per year. I grew up in La Villita, a predominantly Mexican neighborhood in Chicago, IL, and I noticed similar values in other families. But I wished for more. I wanted to do everything but was constantly put in my place and had expectations of a certain role I had to play as a female in a Latino household. This desire for something different drove me to leave home for college and legally emancipate myself from my parents. They didn't understand what college meant for me, and I needed to figure it out, even if it meant leaving my family.

Being first generation, I struggle with the traditions of both our American and Latino cultures. Unfortunately, the central theme I felt, heard, and saw from all the women I met was **guilt**. I used to be so hard on myself for trying to make ALL the school events and sports games, not always cooking homemade meals, or feeling like I neglected my husband and kids. What would my family and people think of me if I didn't produce a perfect product? We feel guilt for not being the best at everything and see ourselves as failures when something goes wrong. How can we disappoint our family after all they have sacrificed coming to this country?

Some women struggle with putting their needs before their families. Is it possible to have it all? And what does it ALL really mean? Latinas are burdened by high expectations. Everyone, including employers, partners, children, parents, and family, has high expectations of us. So how do we not only survive but THRIVE?

I decided to write this book to share my story and the stories of incredible Latinas I've met throughout my career, to let them know they are not alone and that we must all work together to become much-needed leaders. Simultaneously, I want to inform corporate America and our allies about the challenges we face at work and at home.

To tell this story, I will share data on women, Latinos in general, and Latinas in the workplace. Then we'll embark on a journey with three distinct fictional characters as they live and balance work and family. We'll hear fascinating stories from anonymous real ladies with whom I had the pleasure of chatting with. And finally, we'll take some time to breathe, reflect on what was read, and learn about some tools and resources that may help you as you navigate through your own career journey.

DATA

With all my years in the corporate world, I've learned that data is essential for sharing so that people can see the bigger picture. If you are a visual learner like me, you will appreciate this information. This data supports the disparities in how women are not valued and compensated in the workplace.

Women[1]

TODAY, THE NUMBER OF WOMEN IN BUSINESS HAS INCREASED SIGNIFICANTLY, BUT NOT SUFFICIENTLY.

Women versus average men's earnings are 84 cents for full-time, year-round earners

Senior leaders' statistics show that **36%** of women have been interrupted or spoken over, compared to just **15%** of men in the same positions

As of 2022, women only hold **8.8%** of leadership positions at Fortune 500 companies

Women

For every 100 men who are promoted from entry-level roles to manager positions, only **87** women are promoted, and only **82** women of color are promoted

Gender discrimination at work affects **42%** of women

[1] *What is Equal Pay Day? Equal Pay Today, a project of Equal Rights Advocates. 2022. http://www.equalpaytoday.org/overview.*

25 Women in Leadership Statistics (2023): Facts on the Gender Gap in Corporate and Political Leadership. Zippia The Career Expert. https://www.zippia.com/advice/women-in-leadership-statistics/

Gender Discrimination Comes in Many Forms for Today's Working Women. 2017.Pew Research Center https://www.pewresearch.org/fact-tank/2017/12/14/gender-discrimination-comes-in-many-forms-for-todays-working-women/

Women in the Workplace 2022. McKinsey & Company. 2022. https://www.mckinsey.com/featured-insights/diversity-and-inclusion/women-in-the-workplace

Women in the Workplace 2021. McKinsey & Company. 2021 https://wiw-report.s3.amazonaws.com/Women_in_the_Workplace_2021.pdf

Despite significant progress toward gender equality in business, there is still a significant wage disparity. I remember starting my first human resources job out of college at a very traditional accounting firm over twenty years ago. When I walked into the office, it was very clear that it was a White, male-dominated environment. And, because I had access to human resources data for the entire US-based firm, the differences were heartbreaking.

Women are clearly underrepresented in positions of corporate leadership and are leaving at an alarming rate due to bias, isolation, lack of flexibility, and a lack of transition support. There is a perception that women are sometimes overly emotional and can be ineffective leaders. Unconscious biases like these can keep women from being considered for roles or advancement in their careers. Because of these obstacles, women must sometimes find novel ways to advance.

According to a **Fortune.com article**[2], a female executive changed her name on her resume to a male name to land a job. She got this advice from a friend who had gone through the same thing. She received a 70% response rate and started a new job shortly after changing her name. It's unfortunate that we sometimes must make these adjustments to find work.

Unfortunately, as a human resources professional, I witnessed this regularly. Working with leaders who bring their own biases to the table has been a challenge in changing their perspective on gender equality. According to a McKinsey report,

[2] *This Female Exec Changed Her Name to a Man's to Get a Job. Should You? Fortune.com 2016. https://fortune. com/2016/06/08/name-bias-in-hiring/*

men are frequently hired or promoted based on their potential, while women are valued for their experience and track record. When women land a role, they must be visible to demonstrate their skills, land prominent assignments, and build strategic relationships, but women are routinely overlooked. However, when women attempt to increase their visibility, they risk losing their credibility and face criticism for defying gender stereotypes. We are in a no-win situation.

Finally, the pandemic, as we all know, changed our lives. Non-essential businesses closed their doors in March 2020, employees were furloughed or laid off, and schools and daycare centers sent children home. The pandemic significantly impacted working women far more than men by halting their careers and threatening their financial stability. Women experienced significant burnout while attempting to balance their work, children, and household responsibilities. If women leave the workforce, we risk undoing years and years of advancement for gender equality.

Latinos[3]

As the Latino population in the United States grows, businesses see this demographic group as a driver of economic growth. It is critical for both Latinos and non-Latinos to be aware of statistics and facts about the Latino community.

Latinos represent **$1.9** trillion in purchasing power

Less than **50%** of Fortune 100 companies lack a US Latino on the board of directors

By 2050, one-quarter of the US population will be Latino

The average board room is **6.78%** Hispanic

Latino families are **44%** larger than non-Latino families

Latino Americans make just 73 cents for every dollar earned by White Americans

We are the largest minority in the country and the 8th largest global economy

40% of the workforce growth is Latino

[3] *Hispanic Heritage Month 2022 Briefing Book. 2022. https://hispanicstar.org/wp-content/uploads/2022/04/HHM-2022-BriefingBook.pdf*

The Economic State of Latinos in America: The American Dream Deferred. McKinsey & Company. 2021. https://www.mckinsey.com/featured-insights/sustainable-inclusive-growth/the-economic-state-of-latinos-in-america-the-american-dream-deferred#

Latino Board Monitor. Latino Corporate Directors Association. 2022. https://www.latinocorporatedirectors.org/docs/LCDA_2022_Latino_Board_Monitor.pdf

Latinas[4]

When we consider how many challenges women generally face, the numbers for Latinas will astound you.

Unfortunately, Latinas have the largest wage disparity of any major racial or ethnic group. Latinas earn 54 cents

At the current rate of progress, it will take twenty-nine years for the average US company and 238 years for LATAM firms to reach gender parity on their executive team

By 2060, 1 in 3 women in the U.S. will be Latina

Latinas

43% of Latinas are currently spending five or more hours per day on housework and caregiving and a ⅓ are caring for children AND an adult, such as an elderly family member

Only two Latinas have been CEO of a Fortune 500 company

[4] *What is Equal Pay Day? Equal Pay Today, a project of Equal Rights Advocates. 2022. http://www.equalpaytoday.org/overview.*

Hispanic in the U.S. 2022. Hispanic Star Org. https://hispanicstar.org/wp-content/uploads/2022/04/2022-Hispanics-in-the-US-30-MIN-.pdf

Workplace Diversity. USA Today. 2022. https://www.usatoday.com/story/money/2022/08/02/hispanic-latina-business-demographics-executive/10157271002/?gnt-cfr=1

Women in the Workplace 2021. McKinsey & Company. 2021 https://wiw-report.s3.amazonaws.com/Women_in_the_Workplace_2021.pdf

Inclusive Recruiting. Why? Latina Chief. 2023. https://www.latinachief.com/

Although every Latina's story is different, being a Latina in the corporate world comes with some common realities. I'll share some I've experienced and witnessed during my career, as well as those I've heard while researching for this book.

Sometimes we experience code-switching. **Code-switching**[5] is the way in which a member of an underrepresented group (consciously or unconsciously) adjusts their language, syntax, grammatical structure, behavior, and appearance to fit into the dominant culture. I certainly have, especially so early in my career, and I wanted to tailor my work image to my company's culture while maintaining my authentic self, outside of work.

When I started to travel for work, that was a new experience. I've only traveled on vacations to California, Florida, Mexico, and Colombia, mostly as a child. When I traveled to meet clients and colleagues that work in other states, some colleagues would tell me I had an accent, and I'd think to myself, "I don't have one; I speak perfect English," only to realize they were referring to my "Chicagoan or Midwest accent!" I was embarrassed because I was used to defending myself as a Latina.

Working in the corporate world, I feared that my being Latina would reinforce negative stereotypes of Latinos and draw unwanted attention to myself. I was raised, I would like to believe unintentionally, to be seen, not heard, *"Calladita te ves más bonita"* (you are much prettier when you are quiet), which is a widespread belief in the Latino culture for women. Respect for authority, for example, hampered my confidence in asking for that new project or promotion opportunity.

---

[5] *Code-switching: More common than you think and hurting your team.* BetterUp. 2022. https://www.betterup.com/blog/code-switching

I often wonder if this behavior caused my leaders to overlook me for promotion opportunities because I appeared uninterested in advancement, preferring to keep my head down and work. Has this behavior contributed to the meager percentage of Latinas as executives? Do we have to sacrifice our culture and identity to succeed in corporate America?

Sometimes discrimination occurs before we even begin working for a new company. Earlier, I mentioned a female executive who changed her name to a male one on her resume while conducting her job search. Now imagine having a Latino name. Very recently, a good friend of mine with over fifteen years of experience in client management, solid organizations on her resume, and a master's degree decided to look for a new opportunity. When she started her career search, she struggled to receive any hits on her resume. She had two names in her last name, her maiden name, which was of Latino origin, and her married name (American). After months of trying, she decided to drop her maiden name, and within days, she received many hits on her resume and began interviewing immediately.

Over lunch recently, I was discussing my book project with a close friend in the financial services industry, and she told me about an unfortunate incident she had a few years ago. In late 2016, the United States elected a new President, and the cornerstone of his campaign was a promise to build a border wall between Mexico and the United States. When he won, she returned to her cubicle the next day to find piles of boxes on her desk. She was confused, and a few of her White coworkers mocked her, saying, "We built a wall." She was disgusted and yanked down all the boxes. She told them this was completely inappropriate, and their response was, "Oh, too soon?" I felt terrible for her dealing with this type of workplace behavior.

Other stories told to me included how one Latina would receive a job offer after a job interview—but only if she straightened her hair. Another woman's manager told her about a fantastic opportunity, but she should work on her accent before she applied! INSANE, right? Companies must ensure their employees can be themselves in an environment that does not tolerate such behavior.

FAMILIA

Now let's add family to the mix. Latinos have traditionally been very family-oriented and frequently reside close to one another. Some families believe that women can only leave home after they marry, preventing women from going to college and taking advantage of full-tuition scholarships. When I worked in higher education, I met many talented Latinas who were given internships and jobs outside their home cities. And I've seen them pass up these opportunities often because their parents would not allow them to. When I worked as a campus recruiter, we were instructed to only recruit at specific schools to find talent. Unfortunately, most of these schools lacked diversity at the time, putting us at a disadvantage when entering the corporate environment.

Latinas prioritize their families, sometimes at the expense

of their professional goals. They must contend with machismo, the expectation to marry and have children within a "particular" period, and cultural beliefs and pressure. I had children much later in life than is typical for Latinas. I had a college education, married, and had financial freedom, but my family felt sorry for me because I didn't have children. I was then blessed with three amazing children, and my family's perception of me changed dramatically. Typically, when you have a husband and children, your role as a caregiver takes precedence over any job or career. Some women choose not to marry or have children to focus on their careers, which is sometimes frowned upon. The struggle to balance opportunities and family approval is real.

CHARACTERS

———

Now, let's get to know our three fictional Latina characters.

YELITZA LUZA FERRERA

"Young Latina, battling cultural expectations vs. career ambitions."

Yelitza Luza Ferrera *was born in Miami, Florida to Cali-born Colombian parents. She is an afro Latina with rich brown skin and tiny dark locs who speaks fluent Spanish. She is in her early thirties and recently received her MBA from a prestigious university. She is the youngest of three children and the only daughter. Her parents had her late in life, and she is dealing with the responsibility of caring for them. She currently works as a director for a multinational bank and is seeking to advance to the position of vice president. She is attempting to balance her career ambitions and the cultural and familial pressures to get married and have children while taking care of her aging parents. As she seeks to make it into the c-suite, she must also deal with the challenges she encounters due to biases and discrimination.*

The alarm sounds. Yelitza examines her iPhone. "Arghhh, I can't believe it's already 5 a.m.," she laments. "I have to get up and work out because if I don't do it now, I won't get to the gym, and I'll feel terrible the rest of the day." She gets out of bed and walks into the bathroom. "I'm going to see my parents later, and all I need is for my mother to ask me, "¿*Te engordastes?*" (Did you get fat?) "¿*Cuánto pesas?*" (How much do you weigh?)

"Why does my mom always have to criticize appearances, is it a Latina mom thing, or just in Miami, or both?" she asks herself as she looks in the mirror. "Who can say? But it's so depressing." She begins to draw her cheeks back and raises her eyes. "I'm swollen AGAIN! Another late night, but I have an interview to prepare for. I really want to be vice president!"

She sees all her face products as she opens her drawer. "I spend so much money on these things, and they barely make me feel and look younger!" She sighs and looks at her drawer, which is filled with TrueBotanicals, Chanel, LaMer, and iS Clinicals, and is probably all worth more than $1,000. She goes into her bedroom and makes her bed; she needs to feel accomplished this morning. She smiles and gets ready for the day.

As she gathers her yoga mat and equipment, she realizes her birthday is approaching: "I can't believe I'll be 34," she says. Despite everything she has accomplished, she can't help but feel lonely. "Here I am a healthy, smart, successful, educated, and financially secure Latina, who can't find a decent man to date. Why do men find me so intimidating? *Cobardes* (cowards). ¡*Mejor sola que mala acompañada!* (Better alone than in bad company).

She laughs aloud, thinking, "That's what we have to tell ourselves! But a girl has needs, right?" she says, winking at herself in the mirror. She shrugs and gets in her car to drive to the Equinox gym.

Yelitza sits in her Land Rover, thinking about how proud she is of herself for being able to afford it. She starts the car and listens to her favorite DJ Alexsensation, who is playing her favorite salsa song on the radio. "I really need to go out dancing again, it's been a while," she says, singing out loud. ♫ *"Cali pachanguero Cali luz de un nuevo cielo Cali pachanguero Cali luz de un nuevo cielo* ♫*."*

Her mom calls. "Arghh, I can't believe this woman wakes up so early," she thinks to herself. *"Buenos días, mamá!"* (good morning mom) *"¿Cómo vas?"* (how are you?) her mom says.

"Mamá voz sabe que voy para el gimnasio, lo hago casi todos los días" (mom, you know I go to the gym almost every morning) she rolls her eyes. *"Mija, no te olvides levantar mi medicina y de tu papá antes que vengas!"* (Daughter, don't forget to pick up my medicine and your dad's before you come over!) *"Sí mamá,* I know I just got to the gym, I will see you tonight! Ciao.*"*

She wishes she could share how important her day is today. It's the first round of interviews for her company's vice president of investment banking position. Even though she will be traveling extensively, she believes it is time for her to advance in her career. Her family still has no idea what she does for a living; they believe she still opens bank accounts for people as she did in college.

She arrives on time for her class and is relieved that her

favorite spot has not been taken. She prefers to stand close to the mirror so that she can check her form and see her flaws (we are our own worst critics). It's her favorite instructor, Mariah; she works out every part of the body and plays Latin music!

As class concludes, she lies in shavasana, thinking, "That was exactly what I needed!" She begins to go through her mental checklist. Return home, shower, and prepare for the day. She's nervous because she's having her first interview with Katherine, the vice president of another group. She's worked with her before, and they get along well, but she knows she can be tough but fair. She is the company's only female executive in the c-suite. Perhaps she'll be the second. She stands up and walks over to the lockers to retrieve her belongings. Sculpt always puts her in a good mood and makes her feel powerful.

She comes home, showers, and goes into her walk-in closet. "What should I put on?" She wonders. She begins to consider whether she should be colorful today or businesslike. Should she be herself or conform to the norm at work? She starts working on her hair and decides to leave her curls alone. "Ok, I need to get in the right mental space, *Carajo*, I also have my doctor's appointment this week. FOCUS!"

She chooses a light blue suit, a white blouse, and blue heels. She didn't wear much makeup, recalling hearing some men at work make a remark about Sofia, one of the associate's makeup, looking like she was going out on the town. She felt terrible because she didn't say anything and should have stopped the men in her office from talking trash, but she didn't because she had to play the game in an office full of White males. She looks in the long mirror and declares, "I'm ready!" before strutting around the room. "I got this!"

As she drives into Brickell, she recalls that she needs to stop at CVS to pick up her parents' medications. She adores her parents but wonders how she became "stuck" with picking up their medications, driving them to doctor's appointments, and staying at their house when they are ill. She doesn't mind, of course, but they expect her to do everything and never reach out to her brothers.

One day, she decided to ask her mother why she only asks her to do these things. She replied, *"Tus hermanos tienen familia, y tú no y eres la única niña, tienes que hacerlo!"*(Your brothers have families, and you don't, and you are the only girl, and you have to!"

She sighs, wanting to be a good daughter. We Latinas are taught to care for those around us rather than ourselves. She parks her car and stops by the CVS two blocks from work. She walks up to the pharmacy and says, "Pick up for Blanca and Carlos Ferrera, please." The pharmacist checks her computer and informs Yelitza that there is an issue with her parents' insurance and that they must contact them before the prescription can be filled. She also stated that they left a message at the number on file.

Yelitza expresses her gratitude and immediately calls her mother. *"Hola mama, ¿te llamaron de la farmacia?"* *"Claro que sí, yo te dije."* *"No me dijiste mamá, arghh, no me dieron la medicina.*

Tienes que llamarle a la aseguranza." (Hi mom, did the pharmacy call you? Of course, they did, I told you! No, you didn't mom, they did not give me the medicine, you have to call the insurance company). They go back and forth for ten minutes. Her mom finally says, *"Si no puedes, no puedes, a ver que nos pasa, ¡A lo mejor seas feliz si nos morimos!* "(If you can't, you can't, see what happens to us, maybe you will be happy if we died.)" *"¡Mamá! ¡No seas tan dramática! Intentaré más tarde."* (Mom! Don't be so dramatic, I'll try later.) "I don't need this today!" Yelitza says.

Before heading to work, she stops at Joe and Juice for her favorite meal: Green Shield juice with pineapple, carrots, ginger, and the Joe's Club. She must be prepared for the day. While waiting for her food, she remembers what one mentor told her when she got her MBA at Harvard, "You belong there; don't you forget that." I belong. She walks into her office building and smiles, "I've got this!" She enters her office and takes a seat. She was overjoyed when they gave her an office with windows overlooking the water. She will have to relocate to another floor if appointed vice president, but she believes it will be worthwhile.

She sits down and begins to eat her meal while going through all her emails, which takes her until 10 a.m. Her interview is at 11 a.m., so she begins reviewing her notes. She looks out the window and considers how badly she wants this job. She's worked so hard to get here, but her goal is to become managing director, which is still many years away.

She goes over her previous accomplishments and practices her pitch for why she should be the next vice president of investment banking. She's ready! She stands up and walks to the elevator leading to the conference room. Katherine is on the executive floor; she's never been there. She exits the elevator and walks onto the floor, stunned by the beautiful interior design, marble and glass everywhere; they clearly spent a lot of money decorating this floor.

Katherine is visible through the conference room glass, and she notices she is already seated at the far end of the table. "Good day, *Jay*lisa!" They never get her name right, she thought. "Good morning, Katherine! It's wonderful to see you again!" They go back and forth, catching up on what has happened since their last meeting, and then Katherine begins the interview. "So, *Jay*lisa, what makes you want this new position?" Yelitza starts to explain how important the role is to her and how her previous education and experience have prepared her for this opportunity.

As they begin to end the interview, Katherine tells her, "You know, it was really hard to be the first woman to get to vice president level in this small organization, and I really had to change some of the ways that I acted or looked to be part of their culture. If you get this role, you will be not only the second woman to do so but also the first minority to do so. I strongly advise you to make some changes as you progress through the interview process. Even though you have lovely hair, I believe you should straighten it. I believe it will distract the men and you should wear clothes that are a little looser than usual. Oh, and you use your hands too much when you speak; perhaps sit on one hand and then the other, as some of my Latina colleagues in previous jobs have done."

Yelitza was stunned and speechless, but she knew Katherine had gotten the job she wanted and thought maybe she was right. She shook Katherine's hand and expressed gratitude for her time and advice.

Yelitza enters the elevator and rides it to the lobby, where she decides to go for a walk outside. "Wait, what just happened? Straighten my hair, dress differently, and sit on my hands?! I have beautiful curly hair and must change how I dress because I have a lovely curvy body?! Sit on my hands; what am I, five years old? All she had to say was that I needed to lighten my skin!"

She burst into tears because she was so upset. She calls her best friend, Sonya, and tells her everything. "Seriously, *guapa*! That crap still happens nowadays, and in MIAMI, it's like Latin America here! I'm sorry Itza, that is not cool, would you like to go to human resources?"

Yelitza considered it, but she didn't want anything to jeopardize her chances of progressing in the interview process. Even though what she was told was so wrong in so many ways, Katherine was only trying to help her in her own way. Her best friend made plans for drinks after work to continue the conversation. Yelitza wipes her face and walks over to Blo Blow-Dry-Bar to make an appointment to have her hair straightened before her next interview. "You have to do what you have to do, right?" she reasoned. She sobs again as she takes the long way back to her office to collect herself. She needed to get some fresh air and get rid of some stress. "Is this how it will be as I move up the corporate ladder?" she wonders, letting out a loud scream.

"WTF!!"

She returns to her office and sits down to write Katherine a thank you email; she can't help but think about what happened today and what Katherine must deal with on the executive floor; is that truly what she wants? But she has worked so hard up to this point to climb that corporate ladder...a stupid ladder, she laughs.

Yelitza receives a text from her best friend reminding her of drinks at Moxie's at 5 p.m. It's 4:45 p.m., and she must leave; she can only stay until 6:30 p.m. She needs to get some groceries and deliver them to her parents' house before they go to bed. They will not have their groceries delivered by anyone else, and they despise going to the grocery store. They are in their 80s and are slowing down so much that she doesn't know what she would do if they were gone, but she knows they don't have much time left, which makes her sad. Her father has always told them, "Family comes first; remember that!"

She has turned down numerous career opportunities that would have required her to travel 90% of the time or relocate, but she couldn't do that to her parents. She'd die from guilt. Why are we burdened with so much guilt? She thinks. Sonya is already at the table, with two martinis ready for them both. "I couldn't get through life without my girlfriends," she says, smiling.

Sonya is a college friend; they both attended the University of Miami, and she admires her strength. She had a child when she was very young and has worked tirelessly to provide for herself and her daughter without any emotional or financial support.

Sonya is now a director of finance at Google and is doing so well that she can pay for her daughter's private school education. It's incredible how things turn out.

She sometimes wonders if, as much as we complain about how difficult things are, it only makes us stronger and better prepared for whatever is thrown at us. Yelitza tells her everything and shares her feelings about the situation. Sonya listens and expresses her point of view. "Yelitza, you need to do some soul-searching and decide if this is truly what you want. I know you want to be 'successful', and that means being a managing director, but you might not be able to be Itza in that environment. In any case, I'm here for you, and if you need me to kick someone's ass, you know I've got your back!" Sonya begins to remove her earrings and pull her hair up. Yelitza bursts out laughing. "I adore you, *boba!*" The girls finish their meal and drinks and begin to say their goodbyes with a big hug and kiss on the cheek. Yelitza really appreciates her.

It's already 8 p.m., and Yelitza is rushing to her parents' house before they start getting ready for bed and become grumpy. Again, she wishes she could share events in her life with her parents, but they would not understand. *"Deja ese trabajo, busca otro y también encuentra un hombre que te cuide,"* (leave that job and find another and also find a man to take care of you) her mother would say. If she only knew that Yelitza decided to freeze her eggs this month in case it takes her years before she finds the right guy, and she would love her parents to see a grandchild from her before they die.

Also, her mom keeps telling her, *"Me voy a morir sin ver un hijo de ti."* (I'm going to die before, I see a child from you.) So much pressure from her family, if not from her mother, then from her extended family. Her goal is to have her first child when she is thirty-six; she does not want to be any older than that and believes that if she becomes vice president, she will have at least two years in the position. She emerges from her deep thoughts and walks into her parents' house. Her parents are both sitting in the living room, watching Caracol television. They like to stay up to date on what's going on in Colombia. She smiles at her parents and heads to the kitchen to put the groceries away.

Last year, she had to hire full-time caregivers for her parents. They only come to the house from 8 a.m. to 6 p.m., but she realizes that she needs to find evening and weekend care because her mother isn't moving around as much as she can and can't help her much older father. She already pays $3,000 monthly and still must pay her own bills.

Her brothers pay all the medical bills, and she pays for their daily care. She checks their medicine cabinet to see how much medicine they have left since she never called the insurance company. Her parents decide to get ready for bed, and she helps her mom with her dad, then helps her mom. Looking at them, she considers how life has come full circle. They used to look after her, but now she looks after them.

Fernando calls her as she begins to walk home. She sighs and rolls her eyes. "This guy!" she exclaims. She chooses not to pick up the phone. Fernando is her ex-boyfriend from Venezuela.

He was tall, handsome, a businessman, and charming (too charming sometimes with other women).

She recalls the first time she met him. They were at a pool party when he came in, and they found themselves staring at each other. She immediately felt a connection with him, and she has a thing for tall Latinos with ear-length hair, and he was in good shape, as she later discovered that he plays soccer in a league after work. She LOVES soccer, so she was immediately engrossed in the fantasy.

She dated him for over a year and thought he was the one. He possessed many qualities she sought in a man, but he treated her as if she were beneath him. He was also self-centered and did not support her career goals. Yelitza's parents adored him and hoped she would marry him and start having children. She desired more and someone who would be a partner rather than a father. Sometimes she wishes she could answer or even call him to get some attention; a girl has needs, you know. But she knows that in the end, she is only hurting herself and sending mixed signals. She tried online dating, but it was exhausting. There are so many apps out there that it was difficult for her to find one she felt comfortable with.

She gets home and begins to organize her kitchen; her mother taught her not to leave dishes out overnight. It's late, so she prepares for bed and does her nightly beauty routine. She washes her face, uses toner, applies under-eye cream and neck cream, combines two oils, and applies it all over her face, then uses her mini face toner machine for five minutes before applying moisturizer.

She thinks about what we women have to go through to look young as she looks in the mirror. "Heck, if a man was coming over, I'd be shaving, plucking, and putting on lotion everywhere! Men only need to shower, and some don't even do that!" She burst out laughing; she needed more laughter today. She brushes her teeth, changes into her pajamas, and retires to bed.

She lies there thinking about everything that has happened today. She knows she is blessed but wonders why some days are more difficult than others. She is desperate for the vice president position, but will she have to give up her identity to get it? She gets up and goes to get some melatonin. She knows she'd be awake all night if she didn't have it.

Yelitza wakes up exhausted and decides not to exercise. Instead, she lies in bed and searches for money and love manifestation sounds on her Musi app, which her cousin, who is into energy, psychics, and astrology, told her about. It can't hurt, she thinks.

She listens to the music and begins fantasizing about her ideal life...she's vice president of investment banking, making more money and feeling more secure about her finances (including what she spends on her parents' care). Her parents are in good health and enjoying their lives. She has an amazing partner who possesses all the qualities she desires while also being supportive. He is financially secure and stable (she will not be a sugar momma). Despite being a strong Latina, she wants her partner to spoil her financially.

Sonya had sent her a reel about successful women. She

recalls reading that men's stress levels rise when their female partner earns 40% more in the household income and that women promoted to top jobs have a higher chance of divorce. The fantasy bubble burst, and she sighed; it's difficult to be a woman, especially a successful Latina.

Yelitza sits down at her desk and begins reading all of her emails. Her next interview is tomorrow, and she'll be ready for her hair appointment after work. Sarah, one of her female coworkers, came by to inquire about an account they were working on. "I couldn't make it to happy hour last night; how was it?" Sarah inquires. Yelitza asks, perplexed, "What happy hour?" "Oh, I thought they invited everyone?" Sarah says, embarrassed. "Sorry, perhaps they forgot, but thanks for the information, and I'll talk to you later."

She was upset about not receiving an invitation. She discussed her observations with one of her close co-workers, who is White, and it was interesting from her co-worker's perspective. "*Jay*lisa, it's difficult to be white in South Florida; sometimes it feels like we're the minority, but that's no excuse not to be inclusive in the office," she said, smiling. Yelitza understood; she grew up in Miami, FL, and had never experienced discrimination until she went to graduate school.

She begins to prepare to end her day when she realizes she has not contacted her parents' insurance company. *"Hola mamá, me das la información de tu aseguranza? Lo dejé en mi apartamento."* she says. (Hi, Mom, could you please send me the insurance information? I left it in my apartment.") *"Claro amor, deja buscar la información."* (Of course my love, let me find the information.)

Yelitza begins scrolling through her phone while waiting for her mother to return to the phone and decides to reconsider online dating. Her friend recommended this dating app, which claims to be a discreet matchmaking service for elite single men and women. What is it that is taking her mother so long? She ponders. "MA!!" she yells out. Her mother eventually returns to the phone. *"Amor hay mucha información, ¿qué necesitas?"* (Love, there is so much information, what do you need?) *"¡El número de teléfono y los detalles de tu aseguranza!"* (The insurance phone number and your account information!) *"Hay muchos números, ¿cuál te doy?"* (There are so many numbers. Which one do I give you?)

Yelitza thought, is she even wearing her glasses? *"Señora, ¿tienes tus gafas?"* (Do you have your glasses?) Her mom starts laughing. *"Jaja no, deja ir por ellos."* (No let me go get them).

Yelitza rolls her eyes and takes a deep breath. *"Okay estoy lista mija, ¿qué necesitas?"* (Okay, I'm ready, what do you need?) Patience, patience, Yelitza tells herself. *"Okay, dame el número que ves donde dice 'para más información llama...'"* (Okay, give me the number given where it asks for more information call...) Her mom says okay and takes another five minutes before providing the information. *"Gracias mamá, busqué su número de cuenta que debe estar ubicado en la parte superior en el lado derecho de la página."* (Look for your account number should be located at the top right of the page.) Her mom takes another five minutes.

Yelitza looks at her watch; she has a hair appointment in ten minutes and cannot afford to miss it. Her mother returns and gives her the information. She thanks her mother and promises to call her later. She won't be able to contact the insurance company today; she'll have to wait another day. She realizes that every interaction she has with either of her parents can be used in a comedy sketch. Her parents have taught her patience, and she knows she will be where they are one day. She sighs.

Yelitza arrives on time for her hair appointment. The stylists ask her what style she wants to achieve today as she sits down. She tells her that she should straighten her hair. The stylist looks at her and tells her she has beautiful hair, and the humidity will be high this week, causing the curls to emerge. She tells her it must get done and to spray the whole can of hairspray if she has to. She thinks she needs it to last just one day, and then she will be back for the remaining interviews. Hopefully, the interviews after tomorrow will be a final panel interview; she can't continue to damage her hair, but will she keep the style if she gets the job? She is depressed.

As her hair is being done, she looks at her work schedule for the next day. She needs time to call the insurance company before her mom gives her the "guilt trip." She's used to the guilt trip, which can be exhausting. She hopes she doesn't instill the same guilt she was taught to feel in her children.

She gets a little nervous when she thinks about Friday's date; the doctors will be extracting her eggs. She begins to read the procedure she discovered on Healthline, forgetting the paperwork she received at her last doctor's appointment.

"During the egg retrieval, your doctor will use a transvaginal

ultrasound probe with a needle inserted into your follicles under ultrasound guidance. The fluid inside the follicles that contain the eggs is aspirated and collected into tubes, which are then given to an embryologist. The embryologist will examine the follicular fluid and identify the eggs. The entire process takes roughly ten to twenty minutes to complete. Once you wake up, your doctor will tell you how many eggs were retrieved. The number of eggs retrieved depends on several variables, with age and ovarian reserve being the two most important factors. In general, people who are forty and older have fewer eggs retrieved than those who are younger or under thirty-five."

Yelitza smiles, knowing that now is the best time to make this happen. She continues to read.

"It's not uncommon to experience cramping, bloating, constipation, and vaginal spotting during the first twenty-four hours after egg retrieval. Most patients can ease discomfort with over-the-counter pain relievers or heating pads. Contact your doctor immediately if you experience more severe abdominal pain, feel faint or lightheaded, or have heavy vaginal bleeding. Finally, within a few hours of egg retrieval, the mature eggs that were successfully collected will be frozen through a process known as vitrification. This process relies on rapid freezing using liquid nitrogen to minimize the risk of ice crystals forming on the eggs, aiming to improve survival rates."

Her stylists turn her around to look in the mirror at herself. "Beautiful," says her stylist. Yelitza thanks her and smiles, saying that we Latinas look good in any hairstyle and winking at her.

Yelitza exits the salon and goes to get some dinner. She dislikes cooking, but she knows that if she wants to start a family, she will have to cook unless she meets a man who enjoys cooking. She can handle breakfast and simple sandwiches and salads for lunch, but she gives up when it comes to dinner or a fancy dish. Her mother's cooking had spoiled her, and she must start asking her for recipes before it's too late.

She's in the mood for a Cuban *man*, she laughs, but will settle for food. She visits her favorite restaurant, *El Palacio de Los Jugos*, which is both good and inexpensive. She orders her usual *ropa vieja* with black beans, vegetables, and *plátanos maduros* and begins drooling on the way home.

She enters her apartment and settles in. She sits at the table, eating her meal. She begins to consider what she will wear tomorrow. "Remember to avoid anything revealing your figure," she reminds herself.

John Evans, a male executive, will be her interviewer tomorrow. She's also heard that he's a jerk, Mr. entitled. She begins to doubt her candidacy. "Am I qualified for this position? I've only been at my current level for three years. Can I do it?" Imposter syndrome begins to take over her mind.

She texts Sonya and expresses her feelings. She receives a text message that says, "You got this! You're a bad ass who belongs there!" That was exactly what she needed to hear.

Before she starts her nightly routine for bed, she takes her hCG injection, which prompts the ovary to release a mature egg within 36 hours, and she should be ready for her egg retrieval on Friday. Done; she hopes this works.

The second interview is today. She stands up and decides

not to work out again because she will sweat, and her hair will curl. She absolutely must exercise tomorrow, or she will feel terrible. She decides to dress in all black. Short pumps, pants, a blouse, and a loose blazer. She can't help herself and adds a gray necklace; even though it's gray, she needs to add some color.

She puts on the diamond earrings she received as a gift from her parents and brothers for her thirtieth birthday. She wears light makeup, no eye shadow, eyeliner, mascara, and a neutral lipstick, which she considers boring. "You have to assimilate at times, right? Mr. Evans, I'm ready for you."

Though he has a reputation for being overconfident, he did have an impressive background. He's the bank's youngest executive, but she'd heard his father plays golf with the CEO. She's not surprised. That appears to be where all the deals are made, at least according to what people say. She prepares, grabs her coffee and fruit, and heads to work.

When Yelitza enters her office, the receptionist takes her aside. Carolina has been with the company for six months; she recently returned to college and is attempting to begin her career after years of being a stay-at-home mom. She's always complimented her on her outfits and achievements. Carolina wishes her luck in her interview today. "I am so proud of you and would love to see more Latinas ascend the corporate ladder. You are an inspiration to me. *Pa'delante!*"

She smiles and thanks her, reminding herself that other Latinas are watching her and that she needs to set a good example. She goes through her routine of checking emails, returning phone calls, etc. Fortunately, she reserved time on her calendar to prepare. She starts going over her notes and her previous accomplishments. It's time to return to the executive floor. She enters the same glass conference room where she had previously interviewed. She sits down and gets comfortable because John hasn't arrived yet. It's already 11:05 a.m., and he's late. She checks her emails to confirm the time and confirms it's at 11 a.m.

She stands up and walks towards the window. John walks in and says hello without even apologizing. He looks her up and down as she returns to her seat. He introduces himself briefly and begins to question her. She's a little uneasy, and he's acting as if he doesn't want to be there and is being forced to conduct the interview. She does her best to respond to his questions. He looks her in the eyes and asks, "Where are you *from*?" She looks at him, perplexed. "I was born and raised in Miami." "Where are your people from?" he asks. WTF, she thinks as she stares at him. "My 'people' are from Colombia," she says proudly. John informs her that his maid is Colombian. She's at a loss for words. John finishes the interview, gets up, and walks away. It took exactly twenty minutes. "Was that really what happened? Do I tell human resources what happened?" she asks aloud.

Yelitza begins to walk toward the elevator, wanting to cry because she believes she will not be able to continue the interview process. She decides not to tell human resources because it won't change anything. This has been the most difficult interview she has ever had. Is it worthwhile?

She returns to her office, gathers her belongings, and goes for a walk. She needs to think about what happened. She decides she needs to be near the ocean, so she gets in her car and drives to North Miami Beach. The air will be much better for her.

She pulls into a parking spot, removes her shoes, and walks towards the sand. She feels like she's going to cry, but she has to pull herself together for her parents and her doctor's appointments tomorrow. She doesn't want her doctor to think she's mentally unstable to freeze her eggs.

She begins to reflect on her life decisions up to this point. If she pursues her dream of becoming an executive, she will benefit financially, but will she have time for herself, her family, and even her future child? Yelitza must return to work, so she returns to her car. She considers stopping by a *tienda* (store) near her apartment to purchase a lottery ticket; being a millionaire sounds appealing, and she laughs.

Yelitza returns to her office, revitalized and ready to wrap up the day. Sonya texts her to remind her of a blind date she arranged for her tonight. Crap, she says, she completely forgot about it and considers canceling to be prepared for her doctor's appointment tomorrow, but she promised.

She leaves work and returns home to prepare. Hopefully, this guy isn't as cheap as the last guy she went on a date with, who had the audacity to ask her to split the bill. But she was having none of it, so she stood up and walked away, saying thanks but no thanks; he ordered more drinks and food than she did!

Sonya assured her that this man was not from the dating

app but rather a friend of a friend. Yelitza goes through her closet to determine the look she wants to achieve. Because it's cooler this evening, she opts for black spandex pants, a pink sweater, and high heels. She wants to look and feel sexy.

She noticed that her mother had already called her twice. Guilt sets in because she forgot to call the insurance company again and will have to do so tomorrow. She needs to concentrate, so she sprays Chanel Chance on her neck and shoulders; she usually gets compliments from men when she wears this fragrance. She gets ready, gets in her car, and checks her makeup in the rearview mirror one last time. She's a few minutes late, but being fashionably late is her style, at least when it comes to dates.

She finds nearby parking and begins walking towards the hostess, inquiring about the reservation under Manolo Reyes. He was already waiting for her at the bar. He stands up and walks over to her, introducing himself. He's tall and attractive but bald; she prefers men with hair. The hostess leads them to their seats and hands them menus. Yelitza looks at his face; he has lovely eyes and a lovely smile. She notices that he is a little shy but also confident.

He was born and raised in the Bronx, New York, to Puerto Rican and Colombian parents. He attended Columbia Law School in New York and now works in employment law, having relocated to Miami for his job. He's thirty-eight years old, divorced, and the father of a 15-year-old daughter. Manolo makes her laugh, and they appear to share many interests; did I mention he enjoys soccer and used to play when he was younger?

Unfortunately, he recently ended a serious two-year relationship. She sees a red flag but enjoys the conversation. They decided to go to Sugar for a drink after dinner, and he paid the bill. She's drinking mocktails because she shouldn't be drinking before her egg retrieval. She informs Manolo that she will not be drinking today because she has a physical tomorrow.

She desperately needed the distraction and company, and she was on the verge of telling Manolo about her interview situation because he works in employment law, but she decided not to ruin the mood. As he walks her to her car, he expresses his desire to see her again. She smiles and tells him that she would like to, but that she will not be available for another week due to a work project and having to get her parents settled. He opened the car door for her, and she got in after they hugged. They smile and wave at each other as she drives away. That was one of the most enjoyable dates she'd had in a long time.

The next day, Yelitza gets up and prepares for her doctor's appointment. She took the day off in case she didn't feel well. Her best friend Sonya is accompanying her because she does not want her to be alone on this journey. Yelitza checks her work email on her phone while waiting for Sonya and is surprised to see that her final interview, which will be a panel, is scheduled for the following Monday for two hours. She's surprised that Mr. Evans has permitted her to proceed with the interview process.

She takes deep breaths as her nerves worsen. "Focus," she says aloud. Yelitza gets in her car and looks at Sonya before giving her a big hug. "Let's do this!" They arrive at the doctor's office, sit down, and wait. Yelitza begins to survey the women in the office. This is a fertility center, and she wonders if women are waiting longer to have a family because of their careers, and if having a family without assistance is becoming increasingly difficult. She and Sonya get up and follow the nurse when she calls her name. She says, "*Aver que pasa.*" (let's see what happens.)

After the procedure, Sonya brings Yelitza home and puts her to bed. Yelitza has mild cramps and lies down for a few moments. Sonya tells her she'll get some food for them both. Yelitza lies in bed, contemplating what she has done. Her parents would never get it. She recalls her mother nearly passing out when she mentioned it to her. She goes on and on about how babies are made when you are married and have a husband, and so on.

Yelitza realizes she needs to contact her parents' insurance company today. She takes out her phone and paperwork and starts dialing. Fortunately, the operator she spoke with was patient and friendly, and the conversation went smoothly. It never ends! Is her mother aware that the more her parents want her to have a family, the less she can help her parents in their time of need?

Yelitza decides to spend the weekend alone, preparing for her final panel interview on Monday. She calls her brothers and asks them to check on their parents this weekend because she is ill and doesn't want to get them sick. They agreed, and she felt tremendous relief, her guilt gone.

She begins by reviewing all the company's current projects and clients to ensure that she is up to date. Then she goes on to list all her previous and subsequent accomplishments. *"Hola bella,* I know you're busy, but I just wanted to say hello and wish you luck on your work project," Manolo texts her. She smiles, thinking how thoughtful of him to send that. "*Gracias guapo*, you made my day. I'll text you next week, I hope your day is going well, *ciao*," she responds.

She smiles because it feels good to be wanted. Her mother calls to check in and thanks her for resolving the insurance issue, but she goes on and on about how her brothers are good sons and take good care of them. Yelitza rolls her eyes and says, *"que bueno mamá, te visito el lunes en la noche."* (that's good, mom, I'll see you on Monday evening.)

She is extremely nervous as Monday approaches. She goes through her morning routine and prepares her outfit for the day. It's a navy-blue pantsuit with a long blazer to hide her curves. She covers her cleavage with a high-neck white blouse. She's overjoyed that she had time to get her hair straightened over the weekend.

Looking in the mirror, she sees a reflection of someone she doesn't recognize. She usually dresses in bright colors that complement her rich dark skin and uses colorful makeup to make her face stand out. But she looks sad, not excited, and she knows this is what she's worked so hard for in her career. As she arrives at her office, she passes the reception desk and sees Carolina, who gives her a big smile and tells her, *"Pa'lante."* She was in desperate need of encouragement. Looking down, she sees a text from Sonya that says, "You got this! Remember, you belong there!" Yelitza takes the elevator to the executive floor, beaming with confidence.

As she steps out of the elevator and into the glass conference room, she notices four White men joking and laughing. Imposter syndrome starts to kick in again; she tells herself, "I got this; I belong."

She enters the boardroom with her head held high. They begin after all the introductions. "Tell us about yourself, *Jay*lisa." Yelitza begins her speech and kills it. The interviewers appeared to be very interested. Then they start questioning her about her plans to have a family and how she expects to be a mother or wife in the first few years, especially as a woman. They will expect her to always be available for the clients because they should always be a priority.

"Are you sure your family will be okay with these expectations?" one interviewer asks. She tries not to scream and politely answers all their ridiculous questions. Would they have asked if she were a man? "We already have a female vice president. Why do we need more diversity?" she overheard one of the interviewers say. "She has all the skills and experience; she's a great candidate!" says the man. That remark helped her feel a little better. Someone has noticed her!

They end the interview by thanking her for her time. She looks them in the eyes as she shakes their hands firmly to express her gratitude. She walked towards the elevator; her rage suppressed. "Please hurry; I'm about to lose it!" When the elevator arrives, she jumps in and screams. *"¡Carajo!"*

She walks straight to the revolving doors to exit the elevator as soon as it arrives in the lobby. She screams again as she walks down the street. "WTF!" She must walk this off. Suddenly, she receives a phone call from her brother, her mother fell while reaching for something in the kitchen, and they are in the hospital.

When Yelitza arrives at the hospital, she finds her brothers in the waiting room. They explain the situation and inform her that their mother broke her hip, which is not good for someone her age.

Yelitza begins to cry and inquiries about the next steps. They go over the procedure and recovery in detail. She understands that her parents cannot be left alone...ever. Her mother cared for her father to the best of her ability, but she will no longer be able to do so. Yelitza sees her mother and looks at her in the hospital bed, old and frail but still beautiful. She holds her mother's hand and sits with her all night. She adores her mother and recalls the difficulties she and her father faced when they arrived in the United States for her and her brothers to have a future. She is overjoyed to have them as parents.

Her mother returns home after a few days, and Yelitza stays with her to help her settle in. She decides to stay with them until her mother feels better, and she and her brother figure out twenty-four-hour care, even moving them into a facility, something that Latinos don't do, according to her Colombian family. Everybody has an opinion.

While her parents sleep, she and her brothers eat dinner in the living room. They debate what to do, and eventually decide to place them in a senior living home. They sobbed when they realized what was best for their parents. They embrace and begin the planning process. That's the easy part; the difficult part is telling their parents. They agree that her eldest brother should hold the conversation because her parents respect his decisions.

Yelitza returns to the office after a week of emotional ups and downs. She receives an email from the executive director, Jim Cortright, requesting that she meets with him in the afternoon. Did they make a decision? Could it be that she got the job, or a thanks but no thanks conversation?

She expresses her excitement for the meeting in her email response. "*¡Hola guapo!*" She decides to text Manolo. "I know it's been a while, but I was wondering if you were available for drinks this week." While she waits for his response, she checks her personal email on her phone.

She had no idea a recruiter had contacted her about a senior-level position at a smaller firm. Yelitza usually ignores these emails, but this time she decided to respond. She's not sure if she has a future here after this afternoon.

The meeting is about to begin, so she takes the elevator back to the executive floor. She walks into Jim's office and knocks. He's on the phone, but he motions her in. "Good day, *Jay*litsa! Thank you for coming. I wanted to let you know that we were all impressed with how you handled yourself during the interviews and that we received positive feedback from your previous clients. We'd like to offer you the position of vice president."

Yelitza is taken aback by what he said. "Thank you so much, Mr. Cortright, for this opportunity!" she exclaims. "*Jay*litza, we need you to start right away because we have a big client meeting next week that wants to see more diversity and having you there would definitely help us out." She was speechless. "Of course, I still want to see all the details of the promotion before I make the decision," she said with a smile. Jim is perplexed but agrees. Yelitza smiles as she exits his office. She got the job she wanted. She immediately texts Sonya to inform her that they will celebrate tonight with many martinis.

Yelitza received the official offer letter the following day. It details her new salary and potential bonus, which is more than she expected. She gets a lot of invitations to meetings, including some on Saturdays. She takes a seat and carefully reads the offer. She informs the recruiter that she will submit everything tomorrow and will need more time to consider the offer. Her mentor always said never to accept right away. But she isn't feeling well. What occurred? Isn't this what she truly desired?

She receives a text from Manolo as she looks out her window. "Sorry, I've been working on a case; if you're available, let's do dinner and drinks tonight." *"Chévere."* She smiles and gives a thumbs-up. She needs the distraction. Her phone rings as she begins to review her emails. It's the recruiter she responded to the day before. "Hello, Yelitza (she pronounces it correctly), my name is Rachel, and I'd like to speak with you about a position I'm recruiting for."

Yelitza leaves work early to visit her parents in their new home. It was difficult for them at first, but they have adjusted as well as can be expected. They are no longer angry at her and her brothers and have accepted their new home, even making new Latino friends. She notices her parents sitting on the patio, looking out into the lush garden. They have been married for over fifty years. They had ups and downs, but they always had each other.

Maybe one day she'll meet her Prince Charming. If not, she will be the best mother she can be. She tells her parents that she has received a promotion at work. *"Que bueno mija, ojalá seas muy feliz porque la vida es corta."* (That's good daughter, I hope you're very happy, because life is too short.) Yelitza smiled, hugged her parents, and told them she adored them. As she drove home, she kept hearing those words from her mom *"ojalá seas muy feliz porque la vida es corta."*

The date with Manolo last night was fantastic. Yelitza thoroughly enjoyed his company, and it felt wonderful to talk about nothing and everything. She hadn't kissed anyone in so long that she wondered if she'd forgotten how. But she reminds herself to take each day as it comes and not to set any expectations. If it's meant to be, it will be. It's better to be pleasantly surprised rather than deeply disappointed. As she gets ready for work, she realizes she hasn't accepted the job. What is she waiting for? She decides to reread the offer letter and all the advantages of the new opportunity.

Pros	Cons
Executive level	Experience discriminating behavior
Significant salary increase	Expect to work longer hours and weekends
On track to managing director	Even less diversity at those levels
Empower Latinas (si se puede)	Be a token Latina and make no impact
Be a bad ass Latina executive	Have no life

She sighs and wonders why this is so difficult. Yelitza begins to reflect on her parents and the limited amount of time she has with them. As much as she complains about them and the guilt that comes with it, she truly appreciates everything they've done for her and her brothers, and it's only natural for her to be there for them as they grow older. Who cares what other people think; she just wants to be a good daughter to her parents.

She also considers becoming a mother, not because it is important for her mother, but because she wants to live that life. Yelitza aspires to be a part of her children's lives in the same way that her mother was, and to enjoy every milestone they reach. She is young and wants to enjoy life now rather than when she retires.

She recalls a meme of an elderly couple sleeping in a gondola in Venice instead of enjoying the scenery. She laughs. That's not what she wants! More importantly, she aspires to be Yelitza, a beautiful afro Latina with rich dark skin and tiny dark locs who refuses to hide to fit into a culture that will deny her true self. She makes her decision and declines the offer.

She calls the recruiter to inform her of her decision. The recruiter was taken aback but understood after Yelitza explained her current family situation and that she could not accept a position that would take her away from it at this time. Yelitza believes she will stay in her current position until she finds a new job that allows her to be herself. Sometimes you have to take a step back to see what is truly important, and it's okay to make changes regardless of how you expect your life to look. The journey is more important than the destination in life.

Yelitza smiles, thinking that everything is going well and that she is fortunate, and all that matters is that she made the best decision for herself. She goes back to her desk and puts on her AirPods.

"Sometimes things don't go as planned," she says as she listens to one of her favorite songs. *"Los caminos de la vida, No son como yo pensaba, Como los imaginaba, No son como yo creía, Los caminos de la vida, Son muy difícil de andarlos, Difícil de caminarlos, Y no encuentro la salida...."* **(Los Caminos de la Vida ~Los Diablitos).**

MARIA MILAN RODRIGUEZ

"Mid-career Latina, balancing work life and family life."

Maria Milan Rodriguez was born to Mexican parents from Mexico City in Chicago, Illinois. She is forty-four years old and has caramel skin, dark brown eyes, and black straight hair. Jose Rodriguez, born in Veracruz, Mexico, is her husband. She has three children, all of whom are under the age of ten. She is currently a manager in audit for one of the Big Four accounting firms. She holds a BA in Accounting and is a CPA. She strives to be a good wife, mother, daughter, and employee in all aspects of her life. She is attempting to balance the expectations of her family and her employer. She is criticized for her perceived lack of desire to advance to the next level, as well as her family's assertion that family comes first.

An alarm sounds. Maria inspects her iPhone. It's 6:30 a.m., and it's time to get the kids ready for school. She's worn out. Last night was a struggle. Nico, her youngest, was having trouble falling asleep, so she lay with him for a few hours until he fell asleep. She has a client meeting this morning and must arrive at the office early. She goes through her morning routine, wakes up her husband, and then each of her children individually. She then rushes to prepare breakfast, so she has enough time to get ready before dropping the kids off at school. She quickly made scrambled eggs with ham and cut up some apples.

Every day, she tries to serve her family fruit for breakfast and vegetables for dinner. She is the only one in the family who cooks. "Breakfast is ready; come eat!" she exclaimed as she laid it on the kitchen table. She then dashed off to take a quick shower. She didn't have time to curl her hair; she should have gotten up at 6:00 a.m. but was exhausted.

She didn't put much effort into her appearance after she had children. She ensures that her hair is neat and that her makeup is simple. She can't recall the last time she purchased makeup or clothing. Every time she goes shopping, her goal is to buy things for herself, but she always ends up buying things for her children rather than herself.

She quickly dresses, checks on the kids, and tells them to hurry up. Jose, her husband, had left for work. He works as an operating engineer at a few downtown properties. As she herds her children out of the house and into the minivan, she realizes she hasn't eaten anything. Unfortunately, this occurs frequently.

She rushes to school to beat the chaos of the drop offline. As she opens the automatic doors, her children emerge one by one. The parent drop-off chaperone approaches Maria and asks if she can assist next week. Maria, embarrassed, says she can't because of work. "Perhaps your husband can help?" says the parent. Maria smiles and thanks her; we'll see. She turns around and rolls her eyes, knowing full well that he will tell her to do it.

Maria parks at work; she wishes downtown Chicago parking wasn't so expensive, but she has to transport her children in the morning and pick them up in the afternoon. She needs to meet with the partner on her project before the client meeting, and she hasn't had time to go over the project plan. Her kids needed help with their homework, and Nico couldn't sleep, so she was exhausted by the time she finished. Unfortunately, her husband's English isn't the best, so she must assist with homework.

She dashes to her cubicle and begins going over the project plan; she has at least an hour. As she examines the plan, she notices an error and begins to panic. She needs to notify the team, they are meeting with the client in the afternoon. She goes to the partners' office and knocks on the door. Ryan Nichols welcomes her. "Ryan, I noticed the numbers on this project are incorrect," she tells him. "Maria, we thoroughly ran the numbers, and I trust Blaine would have caught any errors," Ryan says, smiling. Maria agreed with him, but she knew he was wrong.

This occurs frequently, she believes; at first, she assumed it was because she was female, but it occurs even when she questions a White female too. She is nearly five years at her current level and hopes to be promoted to senior manager. She will never forget what her starting classmates told her, "Up or out people," so she must advance.

Maria receives a phone call from her children's school. "Hi, Mrs. Rodriguez, Nico is not feeling well, he threw up. Can you pick him up or arrange for someone to pick him up?" "Oh, no, I'll get him right away. Thank you very much!" Maria begins to panic because her client meeting is in an hour. She informs her manager, Tom, that she needs to pick up her son but will return shortly. "Don't forget, Maria, we have a client meeting in an hour." Maria informs him that she will return before the meeting.

She calls her mom while she rushes to pick up Nico. *"Mamá, Nico está enfermo y voy en camino a recogerlo de la escuela, pero tengo una junta muy importante en una hora, ¿lo puedo dejar en tu casa?* (Mom, Nico is sick and I have to pick him up from school. I have a very important meeting at work, can I drop him off at your house?)

She can hear her mom rolling her eyes. *"Por supuesto, pero porque no le digas a tu trabajo que tienes que cuidar tu hijo, ¡eres mamá primero!"* (Of course, but why don't you tell your job you have to take care of your child, you are a mom first!) Maria ignores her remark and tells her that she will be there shortly. Unfortunately, her mother does not drive; she never learned after all these years in Chicago and has had to rely solely on her father or her children. Fortunately, her mother lives close to the children's school.

She dashes into the school, grabs Nico, gives him a big hug, and loads him into the car. *"Mi pobre niño chiquito, mi alma, mi amor."* (my poor little boy, my soul, my love.) Nico's smile always melts her heart. She rushes to drop her son off at her mother's house. She will not arrive on time, perhaps five minutes late. She informs her manager via text message. He doesn't say anything.

She finally arrives at work and dashes into the conference room. She notices two people she doesn't recognize; they must be the client. She also sees Ryan, Tom, and Traci from her team (another manager). She walks in quietly because the presentation has already begun. She can tell her team is unhappy with her, but what can she do? Jose could never leave work, or so he tells her, and will ask why she can't go. She sits there, listening to the partner's update. She wishes they had listened to her because those figures are unsubstantiated. Oh well, she'll fix it anyway once someone else notices the mistake.

Tom requested to speak with Maria as soon as the meeting concluded. They return to his office and take a seat. "Maria, you are one of our top performers, but I am concerned that your family obligations are conflicting with your work obligations." She was sorry, and she apologized to Tom, assuring him that she was fully committed and that it would not happen again. Tom gave her a hesitant look but accepted her response.

As she walked towards her cubicle, she felt hopeless. *"¿Cómo está mi bebé?"* (How is my baby?) she asked her mother, checking in on Nico. *"Está mejor, no te preocupes, su abuela lo cuida bien."* (Don't worry, he's better; his grandmother takes good care of him.) Even though her mother can be difficult at times, she values her and all she does for her and her siblings.

Maria decides to have a career discussion with her husband tonight. She also begins to consider dinner, and what she will prepare for her family. She believes that planning meals for her family is the most difficult task for her. She attempted to plan it on weekends. Her stay-at-home mom friends suggested she spend a Sunday evening planning for the week and freezing the food. But that got old, and the kids and husband grew tired of eating the same thing over and over. She recalls that when she mentioned what she was doing on Sunday, planning the food, not only her mother but also her mother-in-law thought she was crazy. *"Es mejor cocinar comida fresca todos los días."* (It's better to cook the food fresh every day.)

Maria begins to concentrate on her work. Traci, a coworker, comes by her cubicle. "Maria, did you send Tom your year-end performance evaluation? It's due tomorrow, and I'm still working on it." Maria forgot about her year-end performance evaluation, which she thought was due next week. She informs Traci that she is still working on it. She considers another night of work. This is critical; it will help her advance in her career. She begins to panic again, realizing that her conversation with Jose will have to wait another day.

After finishing her day, she walks to the elevator and runs into one of her friends, Leticia, who works in Advisory. *"Mujer,* how are you? I haven't seen you in a long time!" Maria explains that she has been extremely busy with work and family. "SOMOS

Business Resource Group is having an event on Thursday, you should come; they are having a panel with some Latino executives. It'll be interesting to hear how they got to where they are." Maria thought it would be a good opportunity to gain some exposure as well. "That sounds like a fantastic event; please send me the details?" Leticia promises to send it after her yoga class tonight. Maria looks at her and beams with joy. She was promoted to senior manager a year ago and has a very supportive husband who helps her with their child. Her husband is Latino, but he was born in Chicago, which makes him very different from someone born in Mexico. She gets in her car and drives to her children's school (again).

Maria adores her children. Having children in their first few years of marriage was difficult, and then having two miscarriages after becoming pregnant tore her up. It was so difficult to get pregnant again that they tried in vitro fertilization and saw a spiritual lady, but nothing worked. She recalls trying teas, lighting candles, massages, diets, supplements, and anything else that might help her get pregnant. She saw a bruja in Acapulco, Mexico, and she told her not to have any seashells near her. Really! She was in a desperate situation.

Then, seemingly out of nowhere, she became pregnant. Her husband did change jobs, and the stress of it all could have played a role. In any case, they were overjoyed. She desperately wanted to be a mother, and it didn't help that her and his family were pressuring her to have children while not understanding the problem. Her mom says, *"No estabas lista y Dios lo sabía."* (You weren't ready, and God knew.) She then had two more children. Maria is so grateful to have them in her life and she will go to any length for them.

Maria returns home with her children; it's already 6 p.m., and she needs to hurry and prepare dinner. She considers *quesadillas* and carrots as something simple. Jose will roll his eyes; he requires meat at every meal, but not today.

He's a good provider, and they have fun, but his expectations of her as a wife and mother are very traditional to what he was exposed to in Mexico. She walks in and heads straight to the kitchen to prepare dinner. Thankfully, it's quick; she serves everyone and grabs a quick bite before heading to her makeshift office in the living room to begin work on her annual performance summary.

She pulls out a notebook in which she has recorded her accomplishments since the start of the fiscal year. She also kept a folder in her email with all the nice things people at the firm had sent her. Early in her career, a manager advised her to keep track of everything because it's difficult to remember everything at the end of the year. It was difficult for Maria at first because she felt like it was a brag file, and she was always taught not to brag, just keep her head down and work until noticed. However, she realized that while it might work for some, it would not work in her firm.

She goes over the information and realizes how much she has accomplished despite working full-time at home! *"¡Soy chingona!"* (I'm a badass!) she exclaims. Jose enters the living room and informs her that he has picked up all the dishes and placed them in the dishwasher. He can tell she's frustrated. She looks at him, thinking, what do you want as a prize? That is something you should do all the time. She thanks him with a smile.

Maria complained to her best friend Diana about how her marriage is 80/20 most of the time and how she makes most of the money in the household, which she felt was unjust. Diana listened and told her she needed to talk to him because she had already *"mal acostumbrado"* (gotten him used to it) and that if she didn't, it would only worsen. She also discussed the possibility of divorce with her. She believes she can do everything at home and with the kids, and earns nearly twice Jose's salary, so why does she need him? The sex isn't any better, either. She sighs, but she still loves him.

Maria completes her self-evaluation and hopes for the best; it's her time to be promoted; she's worked extra hard this year. She checks on her children, who watch television in the family room. She looks at them for a few moments, grateful but also troubled by a sense of guilt—guilt for wanting some alone time. She's exhausted, but that's a woman's role: to put everyone else before herself.

It's bath time; she still needs to assist Nico because he doesn't clean all of the important parts thoroughly. She's tried several times to get the kids to bed by 8 p.m., but she's only been successful a few times. They've been sleeping by 10 p.m. which prevents her from spending quality time with her husband or herself.

Maria puts the kids to bed and prepares some chamomile tea for herself. Jose enters the kitchen, and she looks at him; he, too, appears tired. She knows he works hard and earns a good living despite not having a degree from the United States. But she needs help. He starts complaining about his job; he's never been happy at any job he's had, but at least he doesn't quit. He would ask himself what kind of man he would be if he did not support his family. That machismo used to be appealing; now it's irritating. She listens and comforts him as she always does. She decides to go to bed because it is late, but first, she checks her work email. She hates surprises, so she checks every night.

"*Pinche* Traci!" she screams as she looks at her email. It turns out that the partner sent an email informing everyone that Traci discovered an error in the numbers and that he commended her for her diligence. She is enraged and frustrated. She noticed the mistake. What should she do now? Does she notify her manager that she discussed this with her partner this morning? She despises these circumstances. If she speaks up, they look at her and say she's dramatic. She is ignored if she does nothing. "I am here; does no one see me?" she screams. Her husband enters the bedroom. "*¿Qué pasa?*" (what's going on?) She looks at him and says, "*¡Nadie me escucha!*" (No one listens to me). He looks at Maria and tells her she's crazy before returning to the family room to watch TV.

When morning arrives, Maria follows the same routine of getting the kids ready, feeding them, rushing to get ready, and leaving for school drop-off. She recalls the movie Groundhog

Day, in which every day is the same. She decided to listen to house music after dropping her kids off. Her brother was a DJ, and she would sit and watch him practice his mixes for hours. She thought her brother was the coolest back then. *"Fantasy girl, you make my dream come true, when I see you moving, I don't know what to do, when night starts fading in, I can't help myself, I dream of you again, don't you know I dream about you girl......"*

She sings so loudly in her car that the parent crossing the street looks at her as if she's crazy. She laughs. She continues, *"No he don't care for you, can't you see you've been used, took your love and stole it away it's your heart that will pay!"*

Back then, life was so simple. She drives to work. *"Jack Jack Jack your body ...."* She is energized, which is exactly what she needs to improve her mood. She wished she could call any of her friends for advice, but no one works in her field, and all of the parents she knows are either in the medical field or don't work and would be unable to understand the politics involved. Maria decides to speak with her manager.

Maria settles into her cubicle and sends a message to her boss. "Do you have a few minutes, Tom? I'd like to speak with you about Ryan's email from last night." He says he'll be available in half an hour. She begins to jot down her talking points to ensure she doesn't forget anything.

She realizes it's time for them to meet. She enters his office and takes a seat. "Hi Tom, yesterday I approached Ryan to let him know that I found an error in the numbers, and he told me that I was mistaken and that if there was an error, Blaine would have found it. Then I get an email saying, Traci caught the mistake." Tom looks surprised at her. "Maria, I'm sorry; I'm sure Ryan didn't do it intentionally. He's been under a lot of pressure lately; it's a big project, and we need to do a good job. I'll speak with him. I apologize again, and I want to ensure we give credit where credit is due."

Maria thanks him and returns to her cubicle. She returns to work, knowing that nothing will be accomplished. But she wants to make sure it was said, and she hopes that he will share this situation when the performance review meeting comes around. She completes her self-review and presses the send button. "Done. I need this promotion," she says quietly.

It's the weekend, and Maria has a lot on her plate. Her husband enjoys soccer and participates in an adult league, so each weekend is the same. She is officially a soccer mom now that her children are also involved in the sport. Her father and uncles were all soccer players when she was growing up. She recalls going to all the games and watching the adults play, watch, and get drunk. Jose's games are in the evening, while the kids' games are during the day. She must plan all breakfast, lunch, snacks, and dinner.

She enjoys spending time with her family and recognizes how fortunate she is, but she can't help but feel sad, alone, and unfulfilled. She has also gained a lot of weight, which makes her feel unattractive. She called Diana, while the kids played, and Jose was occupied with the other dads. "*Mujer*, what are you doing?" Diana informs her that she is attending her daughter's volleyball practice. "*¿Cómo estás María?*" (How are you, Maria?)"Are you still feeling down?"

Maria assures her that she still feels the same way but is not suicidal. She copes by stress eating; she enjoys food. She used to enjoy yoga but hasn't found the time or strength to do so recently. She devotes herself entirely to her family and her work. She doesn't even miss sex; it's been a few months, and she wonders if her husband does. She doesn't care if he finds another woman because it will make it easier for her to walk away.

Mondays are the most difficult for Maria. She realizes she didn't get any alone time and didn't have the heart-to-heart with Jose. She begins the week exhausted and discouraged. As she drives into work, she calls her mother and asks if she can watch the children on Wednesday so she and Jose can talk. Her mother doesn't understand *"tan Americanos"* (how American), but she agrees to watch the kids.

Maria sends Jose a text *"Tenemos reservaciones para cenar el miércoles en mi restaurante favorito Tapas Valencia. Mi mamá cuidará a los niños."* (We have dinner reservations Wednesday at my favorite tapas restaurant, Tapas Valencia, my mom will watch the kids.) He responds, *"¿Por qué?"* (Why?) *"Creo que tenemos que hablar y además hace mucho que no salimos solos."* (I think we need to talk, and besides, it's been a long time since we went out alone.) Jose gives a thumbs-up in response. Maria sighs; she never imagined being married with children and having a career would be so difficult. She expected to be much happier, but it's not all that it's cracked up to be. Then there was the pressure of her mother, mother-in-law, and all her aunts telling her that family comes first, and she should remember that.

Work has been hectic for Maria, and she had not heard from her manager about the situation with her finding the numbers. Traci most likely got all the credit. Her manager arranges a meeting with her to go over the performance summary she submitted. She is a little nervous because she wants to advance in her career. She has worked extremely hard to balance her work and personal life.

She had always wanted to be a partner in Audit since doing an internship with her firm in college. She will never forget one of her female partners. She was taken aback by her presence and the way she carried herself. She was a mother of four children who appeared to have it all. She was well-respected and served on numerous boards, and her children were all successful, or so she thought. She later discovered that they had a nanny and that her husband stayed at home to care for the house and the children. Maria was disappointed because she thought she was a superwoman.

She goes to her boss's office for her meeting. She enters and takes a seat. Tom begins by telling her how proud he is of her accomplishments over the past year, knowing how difficult it is to raise a family, especially a "Latino" family. She thanks him but is perplexed as to why he mentioned the "Latino" family.

"Maria, I believe you are ready for the next round of promotions, but I am concerned about your dedication to the firm. As a senior manager, you will be responsible for managing a team and, at times, the entire project. I am concerned that your responsibilities outside of work will conflict with your responsibilities here at the firm." Maria reassured him that she is completely committed to the company and that if promoted, she will do her absolute best. Tom smiled and told her that while the firm makes the final promotion decisions, he will put her forward for the opportunity.

She left the meeting overjoyed that she was finally being considered for advancement. Her mother became ill last year, and she took some time off to help her mother get settled, and she wonders if therefore she was passed over for promotion. However, another coworker took five months of parental leave and was promoted, Maria only took two months. It doesn't matter now; this is her opportunity. She is going to pray and light some candles because she is desperate for this promotion.

Today is Wednesday, and Maria is dreading the conversation with her husband. But if she doesn't do it right now, she'll explode. She decided to tell him how she felt and to suggest marriage counseling or separation. Divorce would be permanent, and she is not prepared for that. Traci comes by her cubicle and informs her that the performance reviews are scheduled for next week. Traci is also attempting to advance, even though she has only been a manager for three years. Maria would be devastated if Traci was promoted but she was not. She never wishes anyone ill will and hopes that everything works out for her. She sometimes wonders if she is being too nice. She was taught to be seen rather than heard. Has this behavior hampered her advancement at work? She can't even face her parents or her husband.

Maria has been extremely emotional recently. She wonders

if she is experiencing perimenopause. At least, that's what Heather, her coworker, told her. Heather is fifty years old, and she and Maria have previously collaborated on another project. She recalls Heather having hot flashes, gaining weight, and sometimes becoming emotional. Maria has not only gained weight but also noticed that her periods are occurring every few months now, even though she is on birth control. She wanted Jose to get a vasectomy, but Jose claimed that married men do not get snipped or use condoms.

She'd started taking the pill, which she didn't like, but it was better than getting pregnant. She feels like she's in a fog half the time, breaking out with pimples on occasion, which she's never had before; her body aches, and, worst of all, she can't sleep. She tried to talk to her mother about it, but all she would tell her is that *"es parte de la vida."* (That's a part of life.)

She wanted to understand more. She was confused; she had never heard of this, and no one, at least not in her family, discussed it. Maria occasionally finds herself on the toilet thinking, "I don't want to be married any longer," at which point she freaks out and wonders what the hell is going on. She begins researching perimenopause because she needs to figure this out. She's good with numbers, which is why she's in audit, but she has no idea about feelings and emotions.

She reads from WebMD. *"Perimenopause, or menopause transition, begins several years before menopause. It's the time when the ovaries gradually begin to make less estrogen. It usually starts in women's forties but can start in their thirties or even earlier. The average length of perimenopause is four years, but for some women, this stage may last only a few months or continue for ten years. Perimenopause ends when women have gone twelve months without having their period. Women in perimenopause have at least some menopausal symptoms. These may include: Hot flashes and night sweats, also known as vasomotor symptoms (VMS), breast tenderness, worse premenstrual syndrome, lower sex drive, fatigue, irregular periods, vaginal dryness; discomfort during sex, urine leakage when coughing or sneezing, urinary urgency (an urgent need to urinate more frequently), mood swings, and trouble sleeping."* Maria begins to cry; women go through so much.

Maria's workday is finished, and she heads over to pick up her children and drop them off at her mother's house. She rushes home to get ready because she wants to look cute tonight. When she looks in her closet, she realizes that nothing fits. She becomes frustrated but knows she must maintain her composure because it is an important evening. It's either the start or the end of their marriage.

When Jose gets home, he changes his clothes. They get in the car and drive silently to the tapas restaurant. She looks at him and smiles as they take their seats; he's still handsome beneath the gray and dad bod. She still has feelings for him. He looks back, thinking how lovely she is and lamenting the fact that he no longer knows what to do to make her happy. He still has feelings for her. Maria looks at Jose after they have ordered their food.

"Hemos estado juntos mucho tiempo y siento que no me aprecias. Sé que trabajas duro y mantienes a nuestra familia, pero yo también.

Hablamos sobre mí no trabajar, pero ambos sabíamos que eso no funciona y estamos acostumbrados a cierto estilo de vida y eso se debe a mis ingresos." (We have been together a very long time and I feel like you don't appreciate me. I know you work hard and provide for our family but so do I. We talked about me being a stay-at-home mom but we both knew that would not work out and we are used to a certain lifestyle and that's because of my income.)

Jose listens and tells her *"Aprecio todo lo que haces por mí y los niños. Pero tienes que entender, me criaron donde es tu responsabilidad cuidar la casa y los niños no la mía.*" (I do appreciate everything you do for me and the kids. But you have to understand, I was raised where it's your responsibility to take care of the home and the kids, not mine.) She looks at him and knowing this will start a fight, says, *"Sí pero si estuvieras apoyando a esta familia al 100%. Yo soy el que gana casi el doble de tu salario.*" (Yes, but if you were supporting this family 100%. I'm the one who makes almost double your salary.)

Jose starts to get angry. *"María, no entiendes lo difícil que es para mí venir a este país sin saber el idioma y mis credenciales de educación provienen de México. Yo era arquitecto ahora arreglo cosas en edificios. Me encantaría ganar todo el dinero y me mata saber que tú ganas mucho más que yo.*" (Maria, you don't understand how hard it is for me coming to this country not knowing the language and my education credentials come from Mexico. I was an architect and now I fix things in buildings. I would love to make all the money and it kills me knowing that you make so much more than I do.)

Maria understands, she thinks of her parents, but something needs to change. *"Lo entiendo, pero necesitas ayudarme más con los niños y el hogar. No puedo hacerlo todo y empiezo a tener ganas de rendirme. A veces siento que ya no quiero estar casada."* (I understand but you need to help me more with the kids and the home. I can't do everything and I'm starting to feel like giving up. Sometimes I feel like I don't want to be married anymore.)

Jose looks scared. *"Divorcio, ¿Es eso lo que quieres? Te amo María y no quiero perder a mi familia."* (Divorce, is that what you want? I love you Maria and I don't want to lose my family.) Maria tells him that she doesn't want that but she's tired and needs help. *"José, creo que deberíamos probar con la consejería matrimonial. Eso podría ayudarnos a superar esto."* (Jose, I think we should try marriage counseling. That might help us get through this.)

Jose looks at her and explains that counseling is not something he is familiar with. If you're insane and he's not, you go to therapy. What would the rest of the family think? She lets out a sigh. *"Si no hacemos algo, esto terminará en divorcio. Por favor piénsalo si realmente quieres ayudar a nuestro matrimonio."* (If we don't do something, this will end in divorce. Please think about it if you really want to help our marriage.) Jose agrees and asks her to be patient with him. They finish their meal and talk about the kids, which appears to be the only thing keeping them together. She mustered the courage to speak with him; she now feels better; let us now see what happens.

The next day, Maria gives Diana a call and tells her everything about her conversation with Jose. Diana congratulates her and tells her that she did the right thing. "Maria, we need to talk to our spouses. That is not something we are taught. Consider the members of our family. Some couples don't even share bedrooms, and some don't even speak to each other. Regardless of a family's dysfunction, "we" never break it up. Look at my grandparents. They are so toxic that they hardly ever speak to each other, and half the time, my grandmother complains about my grandfather. I always ask her, *"Abuela, ¿por qué no te divorcias de mi abuelo si eres tan miserable?'* (Grandma, why don't you divorce my grandpa if you are so miserable.) Do you know what my grandma responds with? *"¿Estás loca? A mi edad, para qué ahora."* (Are you crazy? At my age, what for now!) And you know what my grandpa says? *"El divorcio es caro. Es más barato mantenerla."* (Divorce is expensive, it's cheaper to keep her.)

Maria laughs but is right we must break the cycle of not talking about things. Diana can always make her feel better; they've known each other since kindergarten. She values having a friend who talks things through with her rather than telling her to do something dramatic, as her other friends do. She imagines Nicole saying, "Gurlll, you need to leave his ass!" That is not what she needs. Leaving isn't always the best option.

In the large conference room, Maria notices her human resources business partner and the partners in her Audit group, including her manager. Traci walks by and whispers, "Year-end calibration meeting is happening now!" She smiles and hopes her promotion will go through.

Meanwhile, the human resource business partner begins

the meetings in the conference room. Karen begins by thanking everyone for coming and establishing some ground rules before they begin. "Today, our goal is to be consistent and objective in evaluating all the managers in this group. We will respect each other, be specific rather than generalizing, I will ask clarifying questions, and keep ourselves on time, and most importantly, everything we say here will be kept confidential. Is everyone clear before I begin?" Everyone agrees.

She starts with the calibration approach and purpose, then moves on to the guidelines for each rating and the promotion process. They review each employee and discuss their accomplishments, feedback, and tenure.

They arrive at Maria Milan Rodriguez. Her manager begins by outlining her performance during the previous fiscal year and the feedback she received, emphasizing that this is her fifth year as a manager." Ryan requests to speak. "I like Maria, but I don't believe she's fully committed to the firm, and she has a lot of family commitments." Ryan chuckles. "Ryan, we consider her performance, feedback, and tenure," Karen adds. "We do not consider her family situation because it has no bearing on our decision." Ryan sighs and rolls his eyes.

The other partners nod and agree that Maria deserves to be promoted based on the data, feedback, and tenure. Ryan says, "She won't last a year as a senior manager." They then proceed to evaluate other employees. Karen concludes by summarizing all the ratings and promotion decisions. She explains the next steps and emphasizes the importance of keeping all discussions private.

As people leave the meeting, Karen takes Ryan aside to discuss his behavior and remind him of the firm's values.

SOMOS Business Resource Group event is tonight, and Maria has asked her brother to pick up the kids and drop them off at her mother's house until Jose arrives. She's excited to meet other Latinos in the firm. She hasn't gone out in a long time without her husband, children, or family. She does not include lunch with her friends on occasion.

She takes the elevator to the lunchroom, where the event will occur. When she walks in, she notices Leticia. Leticia greets her with a smile and waves her over. "You are here, Maria! I'm delighted you came." "Thank you very much, Leticia. I'm delighted you invited me. I had no idea there were so many Latinos in the Chicagoland area!" Maria was utterly taken aback. Did she keep her head down for too long, missing out on what was happening around her? Leticia introduced her to a variety of people from various service lines. Laura Dallago was one of the standouts. She was an Audit partner. She was well-liked, confident, and had two children. Maria sat with her for twenty minutes and learned a lot.

Laura shared how difficult it was for her to get to partner, especially with one special needs child. Maria was taken aback and realized that everyone had a story to tell. That made her feel better in an odd way. She has felt alone in her professional journey, and after hearing so many stories, particularly Laura's, she felt connected to something. She felt inspired and hopeful that everything would be fine. She needed it more than she realized.

Maria got home and felt intoxicated. Jose looked at her and inquired about the event. She began to tell him everything, including the people she met and how she felt. He smiled, knowing how much he wanted her to be happy. *"Estoy feliz de que lo hayas pasado bien. Creo que deberías ir a más de ese tipo de eventos. Te ves inspirada."* (I'm happy you had a good time. I think you should go to more of those types of events. You look inspired.) Maria smiled, *"Gracias José!"* She checks on her kids and is relieved to see them bathed and in bed. "See, he could do this!" she mumbles.

A week has passed, and Maria and Jose have not discussed marriage counseling. Last week's Latino event only fueled her desire to advance in her career. She decides to conduct some research. She needs to find a good counselor who is not only bilingual but also Latino so that they understand the cultural aspect. Diana comes through and finds one in Chicago. "It's a Chicago therapist group dedicated to providing professional counseling and cognitive behavioral therapy to the Latino community in Spanish!" she texts. Make an appointment with them."

Maria dials the number and speaks with one of the therapists. She suggests Maria and Jose come separately for one or two sessions before doing one together. She accepts and schedules her own appointment. If Jose agrees, he must call and schedule his appointment. She needs to stop always doing things for him. Her first appointment was in three weeks. She's already waited this long; what's another few weeks? she wonders, then sighs.

Maria's manager had scheduled their annual review meeting for today over lunch. She is tense and hoping for good news. She desires this promotion not only because she believes she deserves it, but also because what will happen if she does not receive it? Will she be fired? Remember, it's either up or out. They don't say it, but that's how it is. She decides not to dwell on it and takes a more proactive approach.

She became a member of the SOMOS Business Resource Group. She didn't participate in the past not only because she didn't have the time, but also because she didn't understand what they were doing. They had cultural events, but she didn't see the point of learning about different types of food from different countries. It was nice but taking her away from her work made no sense. She now realizes that it fosters a sense of community. She'd been feeling lonely for a long time, but attending this BRG event made her feel accepted, and seeing so many Latino partners gave her hope. As the saying goes, if you can see it, you can be it! She walks over to Tom's office to meet with him.

For lunch, Tom takes Maria to Jose Andres' Bar Mar. She's never been before, but she's heard it's good. Tom begins discussing her performance review after they have ordered their food, and he begins to recount her accomplishments and successes. "Maria, I am extremely proud of your performance this past year. You are extremely talented, and your ability to analyze projects is impressive. As a result, I'd like to inform you that you have been promoted to senior manager."

Maria's face brightens. "Oh my God, Tom, thank you so

much. I am grateful for this opportunity and will not let you or the firm down." "I know Maria, the promotion is well deserved," Tom says with a smile. "I do want to share some areas where I believe you can improve and that will help you on your way to becoming a partner. You are familiar with the work but need to be more confident, especially when discussing the project with the partners. This implies that you don't know what you're discussing, but we know you do. "Do you get it?"

Maria agrees, admitting that she struggled with confidence as a child. "Also, I know that sometimes it is tough to juggle your work and home responsibilities, but I need you to try to find a better balance. I, too, struggle from time to time. It's difficult, but you can hire help, and if you need resources, I can provide some." Maria admires him as a manager, but she wishes he understood that she doesn't have his kind of money to hire help. She could hear their reactions if she told her mother and mother-in-law, she had hired a nanny. "Thank you so much, Tom; I really appreciate everything you've done for me. You've been an excellent coach, and I've learned a lot from you." "You're welcome, Maria; it's been a pleasure; remember, you'll get a new coach now that we're peers." "Do you know who that will be, Tom?" "I'm not sure, but it could be Ryan." Maria overlooked the fact that the reporting structure would change. Ryan isn't a fan of hers, so this will be interesting.

When they return to the office, Maria immediately goes to her cubicle to call Diana. She reveals everything to her. "*Mujer*, we're celebrating this weekend; I'll figure out when in between all the soccer games. "I still can't believe I got the promotion!" "I'm so proud of you, Maria!" You are on your way to partner. We are having tequila shots!"

Maria thanks her and laughs. She then texts Jose to inform him. He responds *"¡Felicidades! Sabía que lo conseguirías. Salgamos a cenar con los niños y celebremos."* (Congratulations! I knew you would get it. Let's go out to dinner with the kids and celebrate.) He means well, but she's unsure how he'll react when she tells him things need to change and he needs to help more.

For the family dinner, they go to their favorite pizza place, Home Run Inn, which is kid friendly. She is filled with love as she looks at each of her children and her husband. She wonders why she isn't happy. Is it her hormones that are causing her to go insane? She has everything she ever desired. Why isn't it sufficient?

They finish their meal and leave. Maria and Jose get ready for bed after finishing their nightly routine. Maria decides to talk to Jose about the changes she needs to make in the future due to the promotion and the therapy session she has scheduled in a few weeks. She needs him to help more with the kids, including meals, and they can't depend on her mom or his mom to help. He needs to find a way to pick up the kids when she can't. She knows Jose never wants to cause waves at work, but she always has to, which is unfair. He needs to man up.

Jose listens and stays quiet. She tells him about her upcoming therapy appointment and how he should make his own. *"Así que tengo que hacer todos los cambios. No sé si esto*

funcionará. Estás diciendo que todo esto es mi culpa. ¡No estás feliz!
Tienes que entender que yo tampoco soy feliz." (So, I must make all
the changes. I don't know if this will work. You are saying that
all this is my fault. You are not happy! You need to understand
that I'm not happy either.) Maria was shocked, she didn't know
what to say. Then she let it out. *"He soportado tu falta de ayuda*
con los niños. Llevarlos a la escuela, cocinar, ayudarlos con sus tareas
y acostarlos. Ahora voy a ganar aún más dinero, así que ¿cómo voy a
equilibrar eso con mi nueva posición? ¿Quieres que me vuelva loca?
Estoy cansada, muy cansada!" (I have put up with your lack of help
with the kids. Taking them to school, cooking, helping them with
their homework, and putting them to bed. Now I'm going to
make even more money so how am I going to balance that and
my new position. Do you want me to go crazy? I'm tired, really
tired!) Jose exits the room and heads to the basement. Maria sobs
uncontrollably. This was supposed to be the best day of her life.
She does not believe this will work out. What exactly does she
do? It's not going to get any better as she advances in her career.

She listens to her favorite Mana song the next day as she
drives to work.

"Como quisiera, Poder vivir sin aire, Cómo quisiera, Poder
vivir sin agua, Me encantaría, Quererte un poco menos, Cómo
quisiera, Poder vivir sin ti, Pero no puedo, Siento que muero, Me
estoy ahogando sin tu amor, Como quisiera poder vivir sin aire, Cómo
quisiera calmar mi aflicción, Cómo quisiera poder vivir sin agua, Me
encantaría robar tu corazón, etc.." and begins to cry uncontrollably.

She adores Jose, but she must also find the strength to love herself. She dashes to the restroom before returning to her desk to clean up. She returns to work, and people stop by to congratulate her; she is beaming with pride. "Congratulations, Maria!" says Ryan. "I look forward to working with you more; we have a lot to do. Consider the office your new home," he smiles as he walks away. She wonders what she's gotten herself into.

Today is her first appointment with her therapist. She's a little tense. She scheduled her appointment during lunch because she thought it would be easier than finding a sitter for the kids in the evening. She enters the therapist's office. She likes how it's set up and how welcoming it is. She meets with Alicia, who will be her new therapist. She thinks she's young, but she has a way about her that makes her feel at ease.

The session lasted only fifty minutes and was more of an intake and information on how they will meet in the future. She likes her and feels good when she leaves the office. "I hope this helps me figure out what I really want or need to do," she murmurs as she walks over to her building. She pulls out her phone and scrolls through pictures of her children; they keep her going; they are her life.

Jose and Maria haven't spoken in two weeks, and the kids are starting to notice. Even though children are young, they feel negative energy, we believe they do not see things.

She decides to approach him. "*¿Cómo estás José?*" (How are you, Jose?) He looks at her "*Bien*" (good). She smiles and tells him that therapy is helping her process her emotions and that it would be wonderful if he could accompany her one day. "*Estoy* *feliz de que te esté funcionando*" (I'm happy it is working for you) and walks away.

She sighs and texts Diana. "Loca, can you send me the information of the divorce lawyer you used?" She responds, "Are you sure? (Sad face). " "*Si*, I've tried all I could." Maria receives the information and calls to make an appointment. She feels she has no other choice. Her family and his will not understand; no one will, especially her kids. She starts to cry "things need to change; I can't live like this anymore."

Maria meets with the lawyer and discusses the process and costs. She informs Maria that this can take anywhere from a few months to a few years, depending on what each party wants or will accept, and that it can be quite costly. "Are you sure this is what you want, Maria?" "I'm not sure," Maria says hesitantly. "Why don't you take some time to think it through now that you have the information that can help you decide what route you want to take? It's perfectly normal." She agrees and says she will contact her as soon as she thoroughly reviews the information.

She calls Diana to discuss it with her because Diana has already gone through the process. "Remember, Maria, your situation is very different from mine. You should base your decision on you and your family's wants." Maria concurs. "I'd like to give him another chance to try to make this marriage work. I'm going to invite him to join me in therapy on Friday. I'll send him the information, and if he shows up, we'll work on our marriage; if he doesn't, I'll take the next steps, but I'm not going to tell him."

Maria sends Jose a text *"Quiero que vengas conmigo a terapia el viernes. Si quieres trabajar en este matrimonio, te veré allí. Aquí está la información."* (I want you to come with me to therapy on Friday. I'll see you there if you want to work on our marriage. Here are the specifics.) He never replies. She sighs and begins to mentally prepare herself for the possibility of divorce.

Friday has arrived, and Maria has completed her daily routine and arrived at work. She tries to focus on her work but can't stop thinking about her Therapy appointment. Will he appear? She begins to suspect that her ambition is getting in the way of what she has always desired: a husband and a family. Should she look for another job with fewer demands on her time? But she's extremely skilled at what she does. "Can't he just meet me halfway? That gives me hope that everything will work out in the end?" She murmurs.

It's time for her therapist appointment. She begins to cry when she walks in and doesn't see him. She was hoping he would make an attempt. Her therapist summons her, and she takes a seat. Jose rushes in as the session begins *"Lo siento, llegué tarde, no pude encontrar la oficina."* (I'm sorry I am late. I could not find the office.) Maria starts to smile and cry and realizes there is hope.

After the session, they went for a long walk and made an agreement. *"Estoy muy orgulloso de todo lo que haces por nuestra familia y en el trabajo. Y lo más importante, estoy orgulloso de ser tu esposo. Prometo ayudarte."* (I'm very proud of everything you do for our family and at work. And most importantly, I'm proud to be your husband. I promise to help you.) Maria knows it won't be easy, but it's a start, and she'll take it.

AMALÍ ROSITA SANCHEZ

"Experienced Latina, balancing career, health, and family."

Amalí Rosita Sanchez was born in Brooklyn, New York, to Puerto Rican parents from Ponce. She is fifty-eight years old and has the option to retire early. She is currently the senior vice president of global partnerships for a multinational technology firm headquartered in the United States. She has a bachelor's degree in engineering, numerous certificates, and serves on several boards. She had three children and grandchildren during her marriage to a Cuban man. On her way to the c-suite, she overcame a bitter divorce, health issues, and challenges to prove she belonged in leadership.

The alarm goes off, and it's 7 a.m. Amalí gets up, still tired. She frequently wakes up in the middle of the night, either to use the restroom or because she is overheated. She is past menopause but still experiences symptoms from time to time. She recalls how difficult it was for her to transition from perimenopause to menopause while also going through a divorce. She remembers being forty-six years old when her periods became heavier than usual and lasted longer than a week. Amalí was in a fog, and she would look at her husband and wonder if she was still "in" love with him. She felt fat and unattractive. She became increasingly emotional, and her body underwent numerous changes. She couldn't sleep, her hair was falling out, and her skin was very dry. She lay in bed thinking about how her life had changed and how perimenopause was the beginning of that change.

Amalí is fifty-eight years old, divorced, and a grandmother. Despite everything, she is content since she has accomplished so much, advanced in her career, and loves her life. She walks for thirty minutes every day, either outside or on the treadmill, depending on the weather. She enjoys listening to her favorite salsa band, El Gran Combo, because it reminds her of home in Puerto Rico. One of her favorites is Brujería, "*Qué me habrá echao' esa chica, Que me tiene arrebatao', Que me tiene medio loco, Que ya estoy enamorao', Quizá serán sus ojitos, O tal vez su caminao', O quizás esas cositas, Que en su casa ella me a da'o, Que tú me tienes temblando de noche y de día, Tú me hiciste brujería, Me quieres mandar pa' la tumba fría, Tú me hiciste brujería, Bruja, bruja, brujita, Tú me hiciste brujería...*"

Even though she was born in Brooklyn, NY, her parents relocated to Puerto Rico for fifteen years before returning to New York. She loves New York but longs for her native island. She finishes her workout, showers, and prepares for work. She examines herself in the mirror and stretches her face in various directions. "I have so many products, all super expensive, but I still look the same," she sighs.

She looks through her closet and decides to dress entirely in red today. "Today is a red day!" She has an important meeting with the new CEO and needs to feel confident. It took her many years to feel at ease with her appearance. When she first entered the technology field, she was scrutinized for years.

She enjoys wearing bright colors and recalls that when transitioning from a senior to a principal, one of the leaders advised her to reconsider her work attire. "I understand your people are exotic, but it distracts the team, and you don't want people staring at you and ignoring your intelligence, do you?" She cried that night, even though it was not the first or only time she had been treated differently because of who she was. She knew it was wrong, but there were few advocates for Diversity, Inclusion, Equity, and Belonging at the time. Human resources would say, "I'm sure he didn't mean it. Try not to be so sensitive" when she did approach someone at work.

Amalí prepares one of her juices. Every day, she tries to drink a different juice. She whips up some with prunes, ginger, spinach, and kale. She's been trying to eat healthier than usual since she turned fifty. Her body was changing so quickly that she couldn't keep up, especially with the achiness. She cleans her kitchen before going downstairs to her parking garage.

She adores her apartment complex. She never imagined herself living in an apartment building. She and her husband and kids lived in a beautiful brownstone when she was married. She had it all: a beautiful home, a fantastic neighborhood with excellent schools, and a wonderful community.

Her husband, Jonathan, met her while she was studying engineering at Cornell. He was also born in New York to Cuban parents. When she first saw him, she thought he was handsome and instantly felt a connection with him. They met at a Society of Hispanic Engineers networking event on campus. He asked her to dance to Yo No Sé Mañana by Luiz Enrique *"Yo no sé si tú, no sé si yo, Seguiremos siendo como hoy, No sé si después de amanecer, Vamos a sentir la misma sed, Para qué pensar y suponer, No preguntes cosas que no sé, Yo no sé, No sé dónde vamos a parar, Eso ya la piel nos lo dirá, Para qué jurar y prometer, Algo que no está en nuestro poder, Yo no sé lo que es eterno, No me pidas algo que es del tiempo...."* and the rest was history.

They dated for a few years before getting married. She had a large wedding in Miami, and both of their families came. She later had three beautiful children with him. It was all she wanted, or at least she thought.

Amalí comes into the office twice a week to stay in touch with her team and leadership, but she does most of her work remotely.

Everyone is meeting with Kevin, the new CEO, today. She

was present during the interview process, and thought he did a great job. She is one of the few Latinas in the executive suite. She recalls her early struggles to advance in her career. When she was promoted to vice president, she did something she never expected to do: She enrolled in speech classes. Amalí has an accent, one of her leaders always told her he didn't understand her half the time and questioned her promotion opportunities.

People were always asking her where she was from because of her accent. She was desperate for the promotion and reasoned that this was what she had to do. She began looking into "accent reduction courses" and discovered some. She enrolled in the course but only attended the first class.

She recalls seeing people from various ethnic groups when she walked in. Following introductions, the instructor stated, "You are all here to improve your communication skills by correcting your accent." She was taken aback. "Correcting?" Nothing was wrong with her, she reasoned. She became increasingly enraged as she listened. People understand me because I've never had problems with anyone except that leader. Perhaps he is the source of the problem, she thought. She remembers crying all the way home after the class ended. She realized that day that she would **never** be ashamed of her accent because it tells her story, and confidence is far more important. When she ran into that leader again, she spoke to him proudly, knowing that if everyone else could understand her, he could also.

Amalí is relieved she could reserve an office space today, as everyone is in due to the new CEO's arrival. He doesn't start today but will be transitioning for the next few months.

She notices that there are others with him, whom she has never met before. She wonders if it's the consultants he hired to conduct a current-state analysis of the company. Kevin requested a ten-minute meeting with the executives in the conference room.

As Amalí enters the boardroom and greets everyone, one of the consultant's requests that she bring him a cup of coffee and says, "Wow, you are really red!" She looked at him, perplexed. "Excuse me?" He repeated his request and asked if anyone else wanted some. Everyone in the room was staring at them. Amalí is one of two women on the executive team; the other has yet to arrive.

"I believe the beverages are outside the conference room; feel free to grab some coffee, and I believe there are pastries as well," she says with a smile. He turns red when one of the executives introduces him to her. He's got nerve, she thought, but she's used to it; this isn't the first or last time. He apologized, and the meeting began.

She is confident that the new CEO will make better strategic decisions than the previous one. They decided to hire externally, so they are undoubtedly taking a risk. The previous CEO was not the best fit for the job and was not a fan of diversity.

The meeting went well, and she is eager to hear his strategy when it is finished. Before the new changes took effect, the Chief People Officer met with all the executives to inform them that some changes would be implemented once the strategy was completed. We knew what that meant: a new CEO means an entirely new executive team. She resolves not to be bothered by it and to continue to be the strong performer she has always been. You can only control what you can control.

The following day, as Amalí was showering, she noticed something on her breast. Her left breast had a lump. Her aunts were diagnosed with breast cancer, and she began to panic. She stood in the shower for a while, ensuring she was feeling something.

As soon as she jumped out of the shower, she grabbed her phone and made an appointment with her doctor. It was scheduled for the following week, and it will be difficult not to think about it. As she gets dressed, one of her daughters, Maritza calls her. "*¡Bendición!* How are you, mom?" Amalí decides not to say anything. Her daughter is about to have her second child, and she wanted to talk to her about something. "*Bendición! ¿Cómo estás amor?*" (Blessing, how are you love?)

Maritza went on to say that she would be visiting her from Miami next month. Amalí asked if everything was okay, and she assured her everything was fine. She misses her children, who are scattered all over the place. Maritza is in Miami, FL, Sylvia is in Irvine, CA, and Angelo is in Chicago, Illinois. Her ex-husband now lives in Boston, Massachusetts. She was the only one that stayed in New York. She always said she would retire to either Miami or Puerto Rico, but somehow stayed in cold weather. She is fortunate to have amazing friends, "*las locas*" to help her get through life.

As women, we understand each other because we share our

deepest secrets, hopes and dreams, intimate details, clothes, and beauty products, and we can be vulnerable without judgment. She did have a "special friend," as well, Michael. She met him flying back from visiting her son in Chicago. He was there on business. He sat in the window seat, and she, as usual, sat in the aisle seat in case she needed to use the restroom; she disliked bothering people.

They began talking because the middle seat was empty. He was a nice-looking White man who was also very friendly. He is a lawyer who specializes in corporate law. He's divorced, has four children, and was born and raised in Orlando, Florida. Because of his job, he lives in New York. The entire two-hour flight, they just talked about everything. He is two years her junior, which she thought was not too bad. She has never dated a "*gringo*," only Latinos or Blacks.

She's always said she wants someone with "*sabor*" (flavor) but Michael is different. He spoke Spanish and spent a year in Mexico after graduating from undergrad before beginning law school. He makes her happy, which she hasn't felt with a man in a long time. They've been dating for almost a year.

After being single for a few years, she assumed she would never meet anyone. Jonathan, her ex-husband, has been in a relationship for three years, which is why he moved to Boston, where his girlfriend's family lived. She watched him move on with his life and decided it was time for her to do the same.

Amalí and Jonathan went through a difficult divorce. When she served him with the divorce papers, he was confused, and he never forgave her for "disrupting his life," as he put it. Her children were in their late teens then, and her oldest, Sylvia, was furious with her. She couldn't understand why she would do such a thing to her father.

Unfortunately, they no longer have the same mother-daughter relationship. She hopes that as Sylvia grows older, she will understand her and what she has been through. During the divorce, there was constant bickering over money. She was relieved they had agreed to split the time and money for the kids 50/50. Her family was stunned as well, and her mother was even more upset when she heard that Amalí would not get marital support. *"Después de todos esos años casados ¿y no obtiene nada del divorcio?"* (After all those years of marriage and getting nothing from the divorce?) She would tell her, *"Mamá, tengo tres hermosos hijos y él me va a ayudar a mantenerlos. Ganamos casi la misma cantidad de dinero, estaré bien."* (Mom, I have three beautiful children and he is going to help me support them. We make almost the same amount of money, I'll be fine.) Her mom responds, *"¡No entiendo lo que estás haciendo, Amalí !"* (I don't understand what you are doing, Amalí!)

She discovered that during a divorce, you lose family and friends. She was even more surprised when her own family, particularly her brother and cousins, stopped coming around and avoided her. She felt truly alone. She is very grateful for her friends. Sometimes family does not have to be blood related. She always thinks of her favorite quote, "The bond that links your true family is not one of blood, but of respect and joy in each other's life" by Richard Bach.

This week, she is trying to concentrate on work. Tomorrow is her doctor's appointment. To calm her, Michael is taking her out to dinner at her favorite restaurant, Balvanera, Cocina Argentina. He has been fantastic. She dated someone after the divorce, but the relationship was toxic. He was married despite telling her they weren't together, etc. She realized they were both in a fantasy world, but it was exactly what she needed at the time. He was charming and romantic, and he made her feel very comfortable. They would talk about everything and nothing. But he turned out to be a coward and an immature man, and she realized he was not what she was looking for.

After that relationship, she dated here and there, but it was difficult to date when you are older. She refused to do online dating, so she met men via friends or through networking events. She dated men at least ten years her junior and realized that despite being attractive, they had nothing in common, but it satisfied some of her needs. Amalí took some time to figure out who she was and decided not to date for a long time. That was hard.

A few days pass, and Amalí enters the doctor's office and waits for her name to be called. Sarah, her best friend, joins her. Sarah has been there for her throughout her divorce, not only financially by providing resources and tools, but also mentally and emotionally. When her name is called, she enters the examination room. She loves her doctor and the office. They made it feel more like a spa experience versus a doctor's office.

The doctor examines her and informs her that she is feeling

something. The doctor orders a mammogram for her. She is happy that her gynecologist's office provides all the services she requires in one location. She is now waiting for her mammogram in another office.

She looks around and notices a lot of women. It saddens her; she sympathizes with these women; we all have a story. She always taught her children to be kind to others because you never know what they are going through. Her name is called, and she enters. She hadn't had a mammogram in a few years. She was so preoccupied at work that she skipped her annual physicals but now regrets it. NEVER skip your doctor appointments. She despised mammograms, particularly the part where they smash your breast; being a triple D didn't help either.

After the exam, Amalí and Sarah have lunch. "I'm terrified, Sarah!" "It will all be okay, *Dios te cuidará siempre.*" (God will take care of you, always.) "Even though my children are all grown up, they can't function without me. Jonathan has found someone to care for him but still contacts me to help with the children." "We can't be concerned about what we can't control. Let us continue to live our lives to the fullest, and if the outcome is cancer, we will deal with it then." "*Amiga,* I don't know what I'd do without you; *¡Te amo amiga!*" (I love you, my friend.) "Ditto!" Sarah replies.

Amalí has found it difficult to focus on her work, but she must. The new CEO has asked all leaders to gather their current strategy and information about each of their employees, including any challenges they face with their teams. She is so proud of herself and her team as she is putting together her PowerPoint presentation. "All of this was done by a *Boricua* with an accent!!"

She smiles, reflects on her career, and is thankful for everything she has been through. She's learned a lot about herself while trying to change her identity to fit into corporate culture and later realizing that she didn't have to, to be successful.

She's most proud of creating a legacy for others like her in the company. She created their very first Hispanic/Latin(a/o) Employee Resource Group. It was a difficult journey, especially in a company dominated by White men. Still, she was determined to create a space where Latinos could meet and support one another in building their community and sense of belonging. She has seen that group grow year after year and loves the organization's increased Latino representation.

Later in the day, Amalí receives a call from the doctor's office informing her of the results and scheduling additional tests. More tests, which is not a good sign. Her doctor advises her to undergo an ultrasound and a biopsy to be safe. She's scared but can't tell her children yet what she's going through. Besides, Maritza is coming this week with something she needs. When one of the other executives contacts her via chat, she returns her attention to her work. "Do you have a few minutes to talk, Amalí?" "Of course, Karen!" "Call now," and they get on Zoom.

"How are you?" Amalí says. "Well, have you heard anything about potential firm changes now that Kevin has finalized his plan?" "Nothing since the Chief People Officer informed us" "What did you hear?" "I heard he was planning to form a new executive team. This does not bode well for us. I'm sure we'll get a nice package." Amalí looks at her, stunned. She can't stay idle; she's sure she can find something else, but she's very happy at the firm. "Karen, I didn't hear anything, so I guess I should start preparing just in case. Thank you for sharing." That's all she needs: no job and the possibility of cancer.

Maritza is arriving today and is perplexed as to why she has come to see her. She would rather go see her in warm Miami. Amalí goes grocery shopping and makes sure to make her children's favorite dishes whenever they visit. Maritza's favorite foods include *arroz con gandules*, fried chicken, and potato salad. She enjoys seeing the delight on her children's faces when she cooks for them. She purposefully purchased a three-bedroom condo in case her children came to visit.

She starts cooking and cleaning the house because her daughter will arrive in an hour. What could Maritza possibly want to discuss with her? She is hoping that nothing is wrong with the baby. She finished in the kitchen and was ready to see her. Her doorbell rings, and she rushes to answer it. They see each other and give each other big hugs. *"¡¡¡Bendición!!!"* "Mama, I'm so happy to see you! You look beautiful!" "Amor, you look beautiful too, and you're glowing!!"

They begin to catch up, taking turns. Martiza shows her mother photos of her toddler and the new things he's doing. Amalí misses her only grandchild. She smiles as she looks at all the pictures. "Mama, how's work going? How's the new CEO? Are you worried that there might be issues? You've been there a long time!" *"Si amor,* work is fine, there is talk about changes, but I'm not worried. It will be what it will be. *Está en las manos de*

Dios. (It's in God's hands.) You're only here for the weekend; tell me, what's going on?"

"So, Joel and I have been talking about childcare since we will now have two children. I would love to stay home with my children, but you know how much I enjoy being a nurse and don't want to leave it. We considered hiring a nanny, but I prefer my children be with family. We would love for you to relocate to Miami and care for our children." She takes a breather. Amalí stares at her with wide eyes. "You mentioned retiring early, particularly if the new CEO would make changes. You can either live with us, or we can find a nearby place to live and pay you. All I want is my children to be with someone I completely trust." Amalí was at a loss for words. "Amor, I'm touched that you want me to care for your children, but I'm not sure what will happen with my job and moving to Miami would be a big deal. I know I said I'd potentially end up there, but I'm not sure when." "I know *Mama.* Will you at least think about it?" "Okay, *mija,* I'll think about it."

Maritza was wonderful to have this weekend, she thought. She couldn't get her mind off what she had asked of her. She adores her family but can't imagine herself ever again watching babies. "I've been there, done that!" When she retires, she wants to travel and live her life, not change diapers, and chase toddlers. However, guilt sets in. Her daughter asked her to keep an eye on her precious children. Her grandmother assisted her mother in raising her, and she will never forget how fortunate she felt to have learned so much from her. Because her parents had to work, *Abuela* looked after the grandchildren.

She enjoyed raising her children and was fortunate to have a supportive husband. She was afraid he'd be a typical Latino who doesn't help with the kids, cook, and so on. Unfortunately, throughout the years, she felt like she was the only adult and was exhausted. She recalls sitting at the playground while her children were all under ten, chatting with other mothers about motherhood. "I read somewhere that motherhood is more than just a job," one of the mothers commented. "It's also a big part of who we are. The pressure to perform flawlessly increases because we associate our success as mothers with our worth." She was spot on.

It's Thursday, Amalí leaves her doctor's office after completing all the tests. She took the day off and went for a walk in Central Park. She is dealing with a lot in her life. She genuinely had no idea that, at her age, she would be divorced, possibly ill with cancer, and potentially without a job. "What will I do with the rest of my life?" She has worked extremely hard to advance in her career. She believes that when life throws you a curveball, you must adapt. She rushes back to her condo to prepare for her meeting with the CEO, which is scheduled for tomorrow. She must present her strategy to him and discuss her team.

She's hungry and stops at her favorite Puerto Rican restaurant, *Casa Adela.* Her mouth starts to water just thinking about the *chuletas fritas, arroz con habichuelas,* and *alcapurrias.* She gets home and starts eating all the delicious food. She takes out her laptop and resumes working on her presentation.

She gets a phone call from one of her mentees, Alicia,

a level-2 engineer with another firm she met at a Society of Hispanic Engineers event in Chicago. *"Hola Amalí, ¿cómo estás?"* (Hi Amalí, how are you?) *"Muy bien linda, viviendo la vida."* (Very good pretty girl, living life.) She laughs. Alicia truly values Amalí's guidance and wanted to discuss Alicia's new job offer and go over all of her options. Amalí made it her life mission to give back and mentor any Latinas who approached her. She learned early in her career that it was critical to help one another and share any knowledge that could help Latinas succeed. Women should support one another.

She will never forget how excited she was to see another Latina on her team, Aletha, when she first started at a small company. She was Cuban and about her age. She was friendly at first, but she soon realized that Aletha was threatened by her, and she even overheard her making fun of her accent. She was so heartbroken. Worse, the other White team members encouraged the behavior, as she overheard one person say. "Let these Hispanics fight it out; maybe both of them will leave." She will never allow something like this to happen if she could help it.

She's all set for the big day! Amalí arrives at work wearing an aqua-blue suit. She is confident that she will deliver an outstanding presentation. She walks into the conference room and sees Kevin and the two consultants; she rolls her eyes because she dislikes the person who asked her to get coffee. "Amalí, thank you for meeting with us; we look forward to your presentation." Amalí smiles and begins her speech. She goes over what they've done in the past, highlighting all their successes, her strategy for this year, and shares some of the challenges they're facing. She displays an organizational chart and discusses what each employee is working on as well as their strengths and weaknesses.

Kevin had a lot of questions, and the consultants had even more, she figured. She finishes her presentation, and the men appear pleased, thanking her for the detailed information about herself and her team. Amalí walks away, knowing she did an excellent job. "Let's see what happens now", she mumbles as she makes her way to her office. Her phone rings, and it's from the doctor's office. She responds, and they inform her that she must come into the office in the afternoon. She knows this is not good news, and she's terrified.

She finishes some meetings and prepares to go to the doctor's office. She calls Sarah and informs her of her plans. "I'm on my way to meet you, Amalí!" That is why she loves her; she is always there for her. They end up arriving at the doctor's office at the same time. They give each other a tight hug. "Everything will be fine!" Sarah informs Amalí.

She is diagnosed with Stage 1 cancer as they sit together in front of the doctor. Amalí looks terrified at Sarah. Sarah takes her hand in hers. "Stage 1 is highly treatable," the doctor says, "but it does require treatment, typically surgery and often radiation, or a combination of the two, and most women (around 98%) will survive their cancer for five years or more after diagnosis."

The doctor tells them she needs to have surgery as soon as possible. Her appointment is set for the next few days. Amalí and Sarah are holding hands as they leave the office. "You'll be fine, the stats look great, and I'll be right there with you through it all!" Sarah whispers. They are overcome with emotion and need some drinks asap. After they order their margaritas at Papatzul in Soho, Amalí tells Sarah about Maritza's request to be her babysitter. "Maybe I should retire and raise my grandbabies, life is too short, and with this new diagnosis, maybe God is trying to tell me something. I've worked so hard in my career, marriage, and children, and perhaps I should take a break." "*Mujer*, you have a lot going on, and yes, you do need to take a break, but you should live the life you want to live, not the life others want you to live. What do YOU want to do?" "Honestly, I don't know," Amalí says as she sips her margarita. They end up laughing for hours on end, which is the best therapy ever.

It's a new week, and Amalí decides to go into the office more often, especially since Kevin is there daily. She notifies her manager that she will be taking Thursday and Friday off but doesn't tell them it's for her surgery. The Chief People Officer, Susan, knocks on her door. "Susan, come in!" "Hello, Amalí! I love the orange on you!" "Many thanks!" "I just wanted to let you know that we (you and I) have a meeting with Kevin on Wednesday. We will review his thoughts on where he believes the Global Partnership group is headed." "Do I need to prepare anything?" "No, he and the consultants have everything they need, I was told." "Thank you, Susan; I'll be there."

Amalí sits at her desk, staring at her laptop. This week, she will not only have her surgery but also learn the fate of her job. She calls Michael and leaves a message; he's been away for a week, and she hasn't seen him. "Mr. Michael, I know we have plans this weekend, but I will need to postpone. I'll be recovering over the weekend after my surgery on Friday. I hope your meeting went well, and I wish you safe travels, *guapo*," she giggles. She sometimes feels like a teenager and will miss him if she decides to relocate to Miami.

It's a beautiful day today, and Amalí decides to go for a walk. She's ready for whatever will come from the meeting with Kevin and Susan. If she gets a package, she may move to Miami and start consulting. She's good at what she does and can't see herself retiring.

She always admired her mom; she always kept busy. She would tell her, *"Si no te mantienes activa, morirás más temprano que tarde."* (If you don't stay active, you will die sooner than later.)

She returns home and takes a shower. She needs all the sunshine she can get today, so she will wear yellow. She prepares her juice and consumes it with a *quesito*. She's been saving this pastry for a special occasion and desperately needs it today.

She arrives at work and checks in with some of her direct reports to see how they are doing. She is aware that rumors are circulating throughout the company and that people are fearful of a reorganization. She assures them that everything will be fine and that she will notify them as soon as she learns of any changes. One of her favorite managers taught her that you should always be truthful with your employees and share as much information as possible. Her direct reports admire her as a leader because she inspires and fights for them when necessary.

Amalí exits her meeting with her direct reports and proceeds to Susan's office for her meeting with Kevin. They must have met before their scheduled meeting because they were already sitting in the office.

"Hello, Amalí. Please come right in." Amalí takes a seat. Amalí, I have to say I am really impressed with everything you have done at this firm, and the clients had nothing but wonderful things to say about you," Kevin begins. "I'd like to inform you that I am making significant changes to the executive team. I've decided to rebuild." Amalí's eyes widened. "I'm offering very good severance packages to those who will not be part of my new executive team. But I'd like to keep you on my team. You have a wealth of institutional knowledge, and I can learn a lot from you." Susan gives her a friendly smile. "Amalí If you are not satisfied with the firm's current direction, I would like to inform you that you have the option of accepting the severance package. As your human resources representative, I am responsible for informing you of all your options." "Thank you, Susan, for informing me of my options. And Kevin, I'm grateful for the opportunity to stay with the firm. Can I have a week to consider my options?" "Of course, Amalí, and if you have any questions, please do not hesitate to contact me," Kevin informs her.

She smiles as she walks back into her office. She calls Sarah and tells her the news. *"¡Felicidades! Te dije que todo saldria bien. ¿Estás feliz?"* (Congratulations, I told you it will all work out. Are you happy?) "I believe I am, but with everything going on, I'm unsure what I want to do." They continue talking for another thirty minutes.

Amalí realizes Michael has called her. She calls him and informs him as well. "Congratulations! I'm extremely proud of you. I know you want to rest this weekend, but I'd be happy to come to see you and help you with anything you need." "Gracias Michael, I will let you know if I need anything. I really appreciate it, *guapo*," Amalí says with a smile. She begins to consider her options. She can stay here and go about her business as usual, or she can use this opportunity to do something more.

She begins with the options available to her:

1. Stick with the company and carry on as usual.
2. Accept the package and move to Miami to care for her grandchildren.
3. Accept the package and launch her consulting firm from New York or Miami.
4. She can negotiate to work from Miami so she can be close to her grandbabies.

She will think about it more, especially after her surgery.

Sarah comes to Amalí's house to take her to the hospital. They discuss her options to distract from the surgery. Amalí you have a lot of options, but I'll tell you that if you leave New York, *las locas* and I will miss you! But no matter where you live, I will always be there for you." "*Gracias amiga* (thank you friend), I am grateful for everything you do for me. I know I must make the best decision for myself and no one else."

They hold hands, as Amalí checks in at the hospital when they arrive. "The operation will take at least an hour, and you can leave today." The nurse comforts her. *"Estaré aquí cuando salgas. Suerte hermana."* (I'll be here when you get out. Good luck, sister.)

Amalí changes into her hospital gown while the doctor discusses the procedure. "You will undergo a lumpectomy, as we already said; only the tumor and some surrounding tissue will be removed. Very common practice and you will go home today." Amali starts to tear up but knows that everything will be okay. Sarah is there as she wakes up, and thankfully, the surgery goes well. She helps her get dressed, and they return to Amali's condo. She is tired and in pain, but she is feeling much better than she expected. She takes advantage of this opportunity and sleeps most of the weekend.

A few days later, Amalí's follow-up doctor's appointment went exceptionally well. They extracted all the tissue, and she will go through three weeks of radiation treatment to ensure that no cancerous cells remain in her body. This experience has truly changed her life and opened her eyes. She thanks God for her good fortune. She considers herself successful not only in her career but also in her family. She enjoys her work, her children and grandchildren are healthy, she is relatively healthy, and she has an amazing network of friends and family.

Amalí knows what she needs to do, and while her job, family, and friends may not agree, she understands that it is her life and her right to do what is best for her. She schedules meetings with Kevin and Susan, another with Maritza, another with Michael, and finally with *las locas*. She needs some motivation, so she searches for one of her favorite Marc Anthony songs and listens to it on her AirPods while riding the train back to work. *"Voy a reír (¡eso!), voy a bailar, Vivir mi vida, la la la la, Voy a reír, voy a gozar, Vivir mi vida, la la la la, A veces llega la lluvia, Para limpiar las heridas, A veces solo una gota, Puede vencer la sequía, Y para qué llorar, pa' qué, Si duele una pena, se olvida, Y para qué sufrir, pa' qué, Si así es la vida, hay que vivirla, la la la...."*

She has her first meeting with Kevin and Susan. They meet in the conference room, and Amalí is dressed in purple today because she feels empowered. "Kevin, thank you again for your offer to keep me on as the firm's senior vice president of global partnerships. I'd be happy to stay, but with some conditions. I keep my current team and request a budget to hire two more people due to the firm's new strategic direction. Also, because I work remotely most of the time, I decided to relocate to Miami, FL, to be closer to my grandchildren while remaining available to fly to New York twice a month for meetings." Kevin turns to face Susan, then back to Amalí. "Well, I'm glad you're staying with the firm; let me talk it over with Susan, and we'll get back to you as soon as possible."

Kevin stands up, shakes Amalí's hand, and walks out of the office. Susan stays behind. "Amalí, I want to express my admiration for you. You are one of our top performers, and I admire your self-assurance, especially when it comes to telling Kevin what you want. You are not only a role model for women, but also for other Latinas in your field. To be honest, I don't see your request as a problem, but I need to discuss it with Kevin." Amalí smiled and hugged her. She smiles as she walks into her office. If there is no deal, she will simply accept the package and move on. "One down, three to go," she says quietly.

Amalí is looking forward to seeing *las locas* tomorrow night. Aside from Sarah, she hasn't seen them or told them about the craziness in her life. She texts them, *"Espero verlas a todas mañana. Estoy tan emocionada."* (I look forward to seeing you all tomorrow. I'm so excited.)

As she looks up, Susan is standing at her door with a huge smile. "Hello, Amalí. Kevin and I just spoke, and I'm here to tell you that he cannot risk the firm not having your historical information and skillset, and he has confirmed with me that he accepts your conditions." "WHAT? That was quick, lol." "Please let me know when you intend to relocate so that we can ensure everything is up to date in the system." "I will, Susan, but I need to plan everything, so it won't happen for a month or two." "That's fine, Amalí; I'm glad to see you staying, and I'm glad to let you know I'll be staying as well!" They give each other a big hug.

Tonight, is her girls' night out. She invited everyone to her house and ordered takeout; she was not in the mood to cook, but she'll make all the drinks. She and her friends took a bartending class during her college spring break. Her favorite drink is the French martini, which she perfected and is now the signature drink of *las locas*. She orders Thai food ahead of time and begins cleaning the house. She ended up ordering cute gifts for each of her friends to thank them for their love and support. She will miss living in New York, but it is time to relocate to a warmer climate. As she grew older, she realized she could no longer tolerate the cold weather. She is looking forward to walking out of her house without putting on layers of clothing to stay warm.

She is glowing with love as the ladies arrive. They each give an update on what's going on in their lives individually. Amalí saved her update for last. "Okay, *locas*, here's my update: my kids and grandbaby are doing well, Michael and I are still seeing where things go, but it's all good, I had stage-1 breast cancer but had surgery and am on radiation therapy and feel fine." Their eyes all widen, as Amalí continues. "My new CEO has asked me to stay with the firm, and finally, I'm moving to Miami to be closer to my grandson and soon-to-be granddaughter." *"Que Que!"* all her friends scream out. "Why didn't you tell us about the cancer or that you were considering moving to Miami?!" Laura questions. *"Amor*, I didn't even know this is where my life was headed. The cancer just scared me, and I didn't want to tell anyone. My kids don't even know. *Sabes que no me gusta molestar a la gente."* (You know I don't like to bother people.) *"Molestar!!* WE are here for you always!" "I understand, and I apologize for not sharing my drama with you all. I was terrified, and you know how I am. I'm Aries at heart!" They all laugh and hug her as a group. *"¡Te vamos a extrañar!* (We are going to miss you!) "I'll return twice a month, so you're not getting rid of me!" She is so loved and enjoys the rest of the evening with her sisters from another mister. "Two down, two to go," she says quietly.

The next evening, Michael picks up Amalí and takes her to El Malicon, his favorite Latin American restaurant. They catch up on life. He inquires as to how she is doing and if there is anything he can do for her. She appreciates him always being there for her when she needs him. He takes her hand and assures her that he will always be there for her.

"Michael, I'm relocating to Miami," she says with a smile. He looks at her, stunned. "What, I thought you were sticking with your firm? Did you decide to look after your grandchildren?" "No, but I would like to be closer to them. I told the CEO I would be happy to stay in my position under certain conditions, such as working out of Miami and flying back twice a month for meetings."

"Is this what you want?" "Yes, amor, I can't take the cold anymore." "I'm relieved to hear that." Amalí looks confused. "I have a confession: I've only returned to New York because of you. I was planning to move to California when I met you. I, too, was sick of the cold. But when I met you, I knew you were special and didn't want to lose you." Amalí looks at him and starts to tear up. "Are you okay if I relocate with you? We don't have to live together; I can find a place there too. I can live anywhere. I will just have a new airport to travel out of." "I'd love that!" Amalí begins to cry. He approaches her and gives her a big hug and kiss. "Three down, one more to go," she says quietly.

Finally, she has her Zoom call with Maritza. *"Bendición!"* *"¿Hola mamá, cómo estás? Te ves cansada. ¿Te sientes bien?"* (Hi mom, how are you? You look tired. Are you feeling alright?) *"Sí mi amor!* (Yes, my love.) I wanted to tell you that I've given it a lot of thought, and I don't think I can care for your babies full-time, but I have decided to relocate to Miami to be closer to you and my grandbabies. I can help you here and there and help you find a nanny with whom we both feel comfortable. I work from home and will be available in the event of an emergency."

Maritza begins to cry. "*Mama*, I am overjoyed that you are relocating here. I really need you, and I completely understand. I know it was a lot to ask, but I'll take you any way I can. I love you very much!" "I love you too, *mija*, and I cannot wait to see you and hug you." Amalí smiles as she hangs up the phone after an hour on the phone with her daughter. Done! she whispers. She made all the right choices for herself. She knows her worth! She has no idea what will happen, but she knows in her heart that she can overcome anything.

STORIES

In this section, we will hear from successful Latinas about what success means to them, their experiences in the corporate world, and how their families perceive them.

MBA Real Estate, Finance & Investments, Author, Speaker, Global Real Estate & Personal Finance Professional with over fifteen years of experience, married with three children.

Being a successful Latina means being where I want to be in my career and having the flexibility and resources to do what I want within my community and with my family. It is about having the time, the health, the finances, and the resources. I'm attempting to open a door for my community.

Few look like me when I sit in meetings, and I want to change that by educating and holding people accountable for being more diverse. It's not easy because I work in an industry that is predominantly older White men.

I was so proud of myself when I finished my MBA. I am a daughter of immigrants and growing up, I was the only girl in my family, where machismo was prevalent, receiving this high level of education. Most White people are unaware of the significance of this achievement.

My corporate journey was non-traditional; I married young, started a family first, and started my career with only an associate degree. I kept hearing that Latinos are uneducated, which bothered me, and I had no role models and no toolkit for achieving business success.

As I was nearing the end of my MBA program, getting ready to graduate, a former manager said, "You will soon realize getting an MBA is the biggest waste of your time." He was someone that had landed the job because he had gone to school with a relative of the CEO. Who he knew and not what he knew landed him his job. I was furious! And my response was, yes, and I can see how you would feel that way if you were a White male with the right connections.

We, unfortunately, do not have that luxury. My education will take me places. I was proud of myself for saying something because it made me realize that we need to start advocating for ourselves and be more outspoken. I can't even begin to think about what my daughters may go through in the future. I hope that they will notice that things have changed significantly by the time they enter corporate America.

When I first entered corporate America, I didn't want to be a part of any employee or business resource groups. I was there to keep my head down and work. Someone in my organization duped me into getting involved in a situation that required assistance for the ERG. When I began to assist, a passion arose from this experience, and before I knew it, I was the national chair for an ERG, leading members across the United States and Canada. It is critical that if you represent an ERG, you educate people about the importance of these groups and explain why they are essential.

I mentioned machismo earlier in my upbringing, but I am so fortunate to have a partner who supports me in everything I do, and he is also Latino! Again, I grew up as the only girl, while he grew up as the only boy. We had a great team, but our families had a different story. I was scrutinized because they thought I was neglecting my family, particularly by his family. I was a terrible wife and mother in their eyes. Unfortunately, we do not have a relationship with his family due to my desire for success.

When I first started school, his mother called MY mother to inform her that I was neglecting her son. With my family, I committed to educating them on what I desired and how, as the only girl, I had to fend for myself, and they respected and assisted me. Interestingly, Latinas are stereotyped as staying at home caring for their families, including our elders. I want to break these generational cycles! What would have happened if I hadn't been so strong and succumbed to the perception?

Another thing we must deal with is guilt. Guilt over not being there for our families as we pursue our education or goals. Even at work, I began a new role and discovered I was pregnant. I hid it because I was embarrassed and didn't know what to say to my manager. When I wanted to talk to my manager about something in the past, she would say, "Let me guess, you're pregnant again." I wasn't, and now that I was, I was embarrassed that I fit that stereotype of Latinas. I was expecting my third child. I finally decided to tell my CFO, a White female, about my situation and told her I was going to quit (it was going to be difficult for me to do it all), and she proposed that I work from home. This was many years ago before anyone had even heard of working remotely. It is so essential for a woman to support another woman! It taught me that you should always speak up because you never know what will happen.

Advice: Make contact with allies. Sometimes we believe we can't reach out to people because they don't look like us, aren't like us, and most likely don't understand. But there is no excuse in an age when resources and information are abundant. People are more aware, and more people want to assist you. Make your case for yourself. Also, find your source of inspiration. My children kept me going, and constantly hearing *"no, porque tu eres mujer"* (no, because you are a woman) motivated me to keep going. ***GIVING UP IS NOT AN OPTION!***

MBA, Human Resource Professional

The definition of success has evolved for me. Early on, it was all about work and getting the next promotion before the pandemic. I felt the urge to accomplish all these things because I am first generation and an overachiever. If I didn't meet my goals, however, sometimes I would take it too hard, and it would impact my health.

Early in the pandemic, a family member passed away from a severe cancer. It was traumatic for me and my family, and it changed my perspective. At the end of that year, I was in such a raw and complicated state of affairs that one thing was clear: it doesn't matter. So much of what I'd put pressure on myself before, didn't matter.

It's important to be self-sufficient and able to sustain yourself, but there's so much more to being a human being. And I think it's easy to get caught up in what we've been told by the media and what defines a successful person as we grow up. For me now, success is more clearly defined. Part of it means financial freedom, but there are numerous ways to achieve that goal. It does not have to only mean climbing a corporate sector; you can have multiple income streams.

Success also includes being aware of one's own needs, as well as those of one's family and loved ones. When it comes to my professional path, I have always been a very curious person with many different talents. I lean into a lot of different spaces. It's all come together in my current role, and from the outside, my career looks carefully planned.

I hate it when people ask, "What's your ten-year plan?" I have taken on different assignments, which may sound wishy-washy to some, but I don't care, so long as my choices are true to myself; I can't be pigeon-holed into a box. While I am still charting a course for myself to the c-suite, I am fully open to pivots to this path.

When I was in my early career, I encountered microaggressions, such as being mistaken as a secretary to someone to whom I was more senior or getting hit on by men in the workplace (especially men in positions of power). The latter was not uncommon at the time, and there was no me-too movement to raise societal awareness about some of these issues.

In a previous role, I had a manager, also a woman of color, who was terrible. She would shut down ideas I had in meetings only to praise a White male peer, who had no college degree but overcompensated with unearned confidence. He would later express my ideas in a subsequent meeting. My other colleagues would observe this and point it out. It was infuriating, but it is an intriguing story because that illustrates just how deeply rooted unconscious bias can be, even among minorities.

In my journey, I also observed an interesting and surprising dynamic with supportive advisors. In the workplace and in academic institutions, sometimes it was White men— executives, my peers, professors—who were the most respectful and willing to mentor me. It was counter to what I would have expected, knowing the institutionalized challenges that exist for women of color and what sources I'd been advised to seek support. The added surprise was encountering some Latinas in positions of power who didn't give me the time of day and were known to brush off new generations of talent. I remember who they are, and I remember thinking to myself, I don't want to grow up to be anything like them. I'll always treasure those women who did talk to me, who took the time to share their experiences and offer words of wisdom. They are the images of role models I keep.

Advice: Take care of yourself, stay open-minded, and set boundaries. Remember that you have a life to live, and, while people will always have advice, solicited or not, to give, only you know your heart's true direction. **PRACTICE SELF-CARE!**

Corporate professional with over twenty years of experience working for an HR Firm, married with two children.

For me, success means being proud and content with what you have. I can't get away from work because I've been working since, I was fifteen. So, the question for me has always been, "Can

I support myself? Can I be self-sufficient?" This includes my family, and financially supporting them.

I associate money as success, which may be a bad thing. But I've always been motivated by the fact that I didn't grow up with much. I needed to start working at a young age because I needed to buy my own clothes and other necessities. I wanted to be in a different situation; I'd have to figure this out, which meant going to school, getting good grades, and finding a job. I've always looked for the next thing I could do to improve my financial situation. When I think of success at work, I think of giving credit where credit is due. I'm successful at work because I give what I'm supposed to give and bring others along with me.

I've spent the last ten years in leadership roles, managing people, so for me, the best way to grow is to help others grow and pave the way by being a mentor. I'm currently at a point in my life where I'm content and moving up to a VP-level position will not work for me right now. I have a young child and a teenager at home, and I'm not sure I'm prepared to balance home and that responsibility. But I believe that when my youngest reaches a certain age, I will be able to reconsider my career path.

I've never experienced discrimination in my career, at least not that I'm aware of, but I have been put in a box in the sense that I fit the picture of diversity, so when we get new clients or big deals, they want me to join because I'm young, Latina, and female, and the company wants to show they have diversity. It makes me wonder if I was invited for the right reasons in terms of my skills or work performance. I've worked from home for the past twelve years, and most of my conversations have been over the phone, which I wonder if it was a benefit because they didn't see me and form a perception or stereotype.

I'm currently the breadwinner in the family, and my husband has more of the home responsibilities because I need to travel on occasion, so he needs to be supportive. My mother is a huge help, and my parents understand because I am the second generation, and they are proud of me for accomplishing more than they did growing up here. BUT, when I consider his family, it's a different story. His father is Indian and a doctor, and his mother is American. His mother never worked, and his father was the breadwinner. So, I get the impression that his family is skeptical of our family dynamics, especially as his sisters are all stay-at-home moms.

I can say that one or two people have been advocates for me over the last twenty years. I've been fortunate to have them on my side. I believe that because I did not have a large network early in my career, I missed out on opportunities. I put my head down and worked hard, hoping that someone would notice my efforts. Maybe if I advocated for myself, I would be in a better position.

I never had a formal mentor, but I did participate in a program for Latinas to grow in their professional development. I struggle with the idea that I should be content with what I'm paid and not make a fuss, and I believe this contributes to the stereotype that Latinas should be seen rather than heard. People will notice my hard work if I work hard, but that isn't always the case. Though the more money you have, the more responsibility you have, so you must consider the balance with your family. When people ask me where I see myself in X years, I always think of my family first, especially in terms of caring for my immediate family and parents.

Advice: I tried to be someone else early in my career because I was afraid to show my true self. We need more diverse perspectives now more than ever. **BE YOUR AUTHENTIC SELF.**

Entrepreneur with over twenty years of corporate experience, married with two children.

To me, success in general is when everything in my life is in balance and I feel at peace at work and with my family. In my career, I have the opportunity to impact the lives of many people. So, success to me is when I touch people's lives and leave a positive mark on them. Nothing beats the fact that my job allows me to interact with so many different people. And after many years of building relationships with companies and hiring managers, they still come to me for advice.

As an entrepreneur, they have that trust, and I believe it is because they believe I am truly capable of putting their professional interests ahead of mine. Every time someone has reached out to me over the years for coaching or counsel, that has been golden to me.

Prior to owning my own company, I worked for North

American companies. I am not from the United States, and one of the biggest challenges for me has been speaking English like everyone else in the room. I have the most difficulty when I am surrounded by White males. And I constantly get the impression that something is wrong with my English, my accent, or whatever else.

I was always nervous, especially at the start of my career. I couldn't make peace with it until I learned to accept it. Because I am not a native English speaker, this will not change. But that happened recently, and it was one of the most difficult challenges for me, along with being able to express myself, communicate my thoughts and ideas, and be as articulate as I am in Spanish.

I recall a situation when I was hired by this corporation, and I was the only Latina on their management team. I was hired as a partner by the firm. They didn't have any Latinas at the time, so they tried to recruit me for five years; they really wanted me to come to the firm. I had my own company at the time, and I decided to sell my portion of it to my partner.

At first, they called me for everything. I recall a virtual meeting in which the CEO was going to speak to about 400 partners around the world, and they wanted five people to be the main speakers, and they called me; I was super proud. Then I realized that whenever they needed to demonstrate diversity, they always called on me. When I repeatedly asked to be a part of specific projects, I was always turned down. That's when I realized I was the token Latina. It was difficult for me to accept.

Another time there was a project aimed at the Latino/

Hispanic market, and they would ask for my input but not invite me to meetings; they had me working behind the scenes! My name was not going to be included in a large communication, but they wanted me to promote the project. I started to feel uneasy being there, which is difficult because I went in with such enthusiasm. They only wanted to demonstrate to the organization that they were diversifying the leadership team. All decisions were made without my input by White males. I stayed for a little over a year before leaving; I couldn't take it anymore. It was destroying my soul and spirit. I, too, felt as if I had betrayed myself.

You know, I should have seen this, but I really didn't expect this. I blamed myself. Did I make a BIG mistake? I should have said something! I never discussed it with anyone because I was so afraid. There I was, feeling as though I had nothing to contribute. I didn't even tell my husband about this until I made the decision to leave. My pride took over; I'd been successful my entire career, so this was a setback for me, and I was embarrassed.

But in my exit interview I made sure in a polite way to express what my experience had been and gave many examples. I found the strength to leave, and I said I will never compromise my dignity. But now I consider it to be the best thing that ever happened to me, because it led to what I'm doing now, which is running my own business again. I promised myself that I would never again be tokenized by any corporation.

My family had a different opinion about what I should do with my career. My parents didn't want me to go to college because their families were entrepreneurs who didn't understand the concept of paying for college rather than working after high school. My parents told me they couldn't afford to pay for my college education, but I found a way. I even had to borrow money from a friend to pay for college admissions exams.

I knew I needed to learn English before going to college, so I came to the United States on a program my senior year of high school. They thought I was insane, and it was my grandmother who gave me the money! So, I went to the east coast as an exchange student, and it was also my first experience with cold weather. Unfortunately, after a few months, I realized they only wanted me as their nanny, so I contacted the director in my home country, who thankfully relocated me to another family. I experienced biases against Latinas for the first time. Everything has been extremely rewarding and all your experiences shape who you are.

Advice: DON'T EVER COMPROMISE WHO YOU ARE! Even if it's painful or frightening. Bring your complete identity, including how you look, speak, dress, and act.

Human Resources professional with ten years of experience, primarily in the accounting industry, married with two children.

For me, success means learning something new and succeeding in it. I'm very motivated and expect to see results. This has also been incorporated into my work. I do believe that success is correlated with wealth, so when I met a certain salary goal, I was proud of myself, but then wondered what came next.

I've had a successful career because I pushed myself to try new things even when I was afraid, I didn't belong or possessed the necessary skillset. However, I recently realized that managing both my career and my family is a higher priority. Because my children are so young, I am unable to prioritize my career. I struggled with imposter syndrome early in my career, and it was the source of my insecurity for a long time.

My parents didn't finish high school. I was the only one of a few of my friends who went to college, and I wasn't really surrounded by "professionals," (besides my mom) so I was always unsure of how I spoke, especially in a corporate environment. I felt I needed to do some code switching because I'm a very different person at work than I am at home.

So, do I bring my true self to work? Not really. It has helped to have a black leader; I feel she understands me better. "Us brown ladies, we have to work a little differently here!" she said. I must remember not to forget where I came from while also learning how to behave differently in a professional setting. I had a White partner once who was very passive aggressive and ignored me almost entirely. Every morning, I would greet her, but she would never respond. Even though it was early in my career, I still mattered.

Years later, when I took over as her business partner in human resources, I found she was concerned with my level and that, if I weren't at "hers," I wasn't significant. Now that I constantly work with her, we get along. We, women, should be helping each other. I took it personally, thinking it was me, and I worked hard for years to get her to acknowledge me and to think I wanted to be like her because she made it seem easy to be a partner and balance work and a family.

At home, I do face some difficulties with my spouse. He is Latino and has a different perspective on what my role should be, and he also does not understand the corporate world. He is first generation and the first in his family to graduate from college. He's supportive up until it affects him, the house, and the kids. So, it's still a long road ahead of us, but we're trying to figure it out. What's more difficult is that I make more money than he does, and it's a subject we never discuss. He'd prefer that I not be the breadwinner and spend all my time at home cooking, cleaning, and being a mother; that is what his mom did after all. But we'd have a different way of life, and he's not ready for that. My mother is very proud of me, but she wishes I would have married someone who would take care of me, financially. I'm still trying to figure out how I manage to work two full-time jobs (corporate and home). But that's what we do sometimes, especially us Latinas: We make it work somehow.

Advice: Don't allow impostor syndrome to diminish your abilities and capabilities; instead, **ACCEPT THE UNCOMFORTABLE BECAUSE IT WILL HELP YOU LEARN NEW THINGS AND HELP YOU ADVANCE IN YOUR CAREER.**

MBA, Real Estate Executive with over twenty years of experience, with two children.

Being successful to me means being confident in myself and my abilities. How I provide for myself, my independence, and what I provide for others, especially my loved ones. You already know how important family is for Latinos. So that's what life is all about. And every time there is a death in the family, you are reminded of your priorities. Now my professional success is defined by a position, a job, and a company that allows me the ability to really make a difference and really influence and do something and to be able to have a well-rounded life—being generally happy and fulfilled, knowing that our voices are heard, and having a platform to convey information and give and receive from our team. I have spent times in my career when I am stretched. We, like most women, try to do everything, only to realize that we're doing everything half-heartedly and not to the best of our abilities.

I'm the first person in my family to attend and graduate from college. When I first started working, I didn't know anyone. So, getting in the door was difficult. Fortunately, I was able to transition into an analyst position. I was hired alongside my peers from across the country for an insurance company, and being a minority stood out; the attendees were majority from Ivy League universities which usually meant mostly White people. I stood out from everyone else in the room.

I believed that I had to portray myself well. The majority of Latinas are taught to be modest. We were taught to be extremely respectful. As a result, I became shyer, and hesitant to speak up in meetings. My manager also brought it up as something I needed to focus on, so it was something I was aware I needed to do.

I joined Toastmasters, and it was amazing for me. It was terrifying and overwhelming initially, but one of my lawyer coworkers attended it with me and was very supportive. I mentioned before that Latinas are raised in a particular way, which affects us in the workforce. Therefore, I have always encouraged people to take advantage of Toastmasters.

I'd just put my head down, do my work, and hope to be noticed. However, as you are aware, this is not the corporate culture. You must speak up. I didn't say as much. And, of course, when I did speak up, I was afraid of making mistakes or saying the wrong things. As a result, I would mentally repeat sentences several times before speaking, which, in retrospect, caused me to suffer far more than necessary. But it's all part of the process. It's part of venturing out and not having those role models.

I didn't have a formal mentor, but I've had many informal mentors, people I could talk to, both men and women. I became a member of the National Society of Hispanic MBAs at the time and have participated in some ERGs back then and witnessed their evolution. I am currently involved in the Latino ERG and the Women's ERG, both of which bring different perspectives.

With my family, it fascinates me that they still ask me what I do after all these years! I come from a large family and am the only one with a BA and an MBA. My family, particularly my father, was very proud of me. I was fortunate to travel internationally and invited my parents on occasion, and they were amazed by the opportunities that were provided to me to do this. I was so happy to show my family a different way of living.

I met my non-Hispanic husband in college then, and we were both focused on our careers, so we didn't plan on having kids right away. Every Thanksgiving, my family would put pressure on me; my father would ask me when will the children come, and he was very concerned my biological clock was ticking. As you can imagine, I did not look forward to Thanksgiving at times.

Years later, I had children and entered a different life stage. You can see how difficult it is to get your work-life balance right. You now have much less leeway to stay late and so on. So those were difficult years. I was fortunate enough to be able to hire a nanny to come to my house, which was the best thing for my family. I began traveling frequently, particularly to Latin America, when my children were very young. Though my husband was supportive at the time, he always asked why my family would not help, and I would turn the tables and ask him why his family did not help. I asked him if he wanted me to stop working, and he said no because I made more money than he did. I also wanted my children to see me as a self-sufficient career woman and a role model for them. It's funny how things don't always turn out the way you expect them to.

Advice: I'm all for empowering my children and the next generation to think differently. Just because our culture has done things a certain way for so long doesn't mean that's the only way. **LIFE CHANGES, AND WE HAVE TO LEARN TO CHANGE WITH IT!**

REFLECTION AND RESOURCES

Whom do you resonate with? Can you relate to any of it now that you've read the statistics, peeked into the lives of three fictional characters, and heard the stories of various Latina professionals? Were you ever in a situation like Yelitza's where you had to consider your parents' care before making career decisions? Or should you change your appearance to fit in with the company culture? Did you identify with Maria in terms of having a strong desire to advance but lacking the support of your family to do so? Did you share any characteristics with Amali's struggle to blend family, job, and self-care while adjusting to a culture where her accent is not the norm? **What does success look like for you?**

Throughout my corporate career, my definition of success has changed several times. I've realized that I'm more than just a title. Even though I was stagnant in my career for many years to raise three wonderful children, I consider myself successful in my field. When I was married, I also tried to link my success to that of my husband, and I learned that I should not put expectations on others and should not rely on others for my own success. I'm content with what I'm doing and where I'm going, including empowering other women. You must find out what success means for you. But you must start with yourself. Know your worth, and you will succeed!

Where to begin? There are numerous factors to consider, but I believe the four listed below are a good starting point.

Mental Health - Let's face it: We don't discuss mental health as much as we should. I remember telling my mother about my therapist visits a few years ago. She says to me *"No deberías estar hablando con extraños. Dame el dinero. Puedes hablar conmigo."* (You should not be talking to strangers. Give me the money. You can talk to me.) I'd tease her, asking how to talk to her about her. As you might expect, this did not sit well with her. There is a widespread belief among Latinos, especially the older generation, that discussing mental health will be an embarrassment and shame for the family. We need to change this belief. How can we be productive in the world if we don't feel good in our own skin? First, you need to find the right therapist for you. It was very important for me to have a Latina therapist years ago. This person understood the Latino culture and could relate to my situation. She was extremely helpful in my journey to accept myself, and I greatly valued my time with her. If you need to talk to someone, here's a good place to start. https://latinxtherapy.com/

"I think it's really important to take the stigma away from mental health… My brain and my heart are really important to me. I don't know why I wouldn't seek help to have those things be as healthy as my teeth?"—Kerry Washington

Confidence - Being self-assured entails fully knowing and accepting oneself, as well as accepting one's strengths and weaknesses. **NO ONE IS PERFECT, INCLUDING YOU, AND THAT'S OKAY!** Allow yourself some leeway if things don't go as planned; revisit, reevaluate, and try again. You must be ok with the uncomfortable and remember to take things one day at a time. Stop the negative talk; we can be our harshest critics sometimes, and you are not alone in this. I have to remind myself all the time. Remember, attitude is everything. As I strive to empower more Latinas, I'd like to point out that there are numerous books written by Latina authors that may be able to help you on your journey to self-confidence and self-love. Here are just a few.

- *I Am Diosa by Christin Gutierrez* - A journey to healing deep, loving yourself, and returning home to your soul.
- *Break The Good Girl Myth by Majo Molfino* - How to dismantle outdated rules, unleash your power, and design a more purposeful life.
- *What Would Frida do? by Arianna Davis* - A guide to living boldly.
- *Chica, Why Not? by Sandra Hinojosa Ludwig* - How to live with intention and manifest a life that loves you back.

"Enamórate de ti, de la vida, y luego de quien quieras"
- Frida Khalo

Education - Education provides stability in life, which no one can ever take away from you. Being well-educated increases your chances of landing a better opportunity and opening new doors for yourself. If you can't afford to go to school, read everything you can about your interests. Investigate some colleges and universities for programs or scholarships. Check with your employer; most offer some form of tuition reimbursement. Numerous websites also offer low-cost training.

- **LinkedIn** - https://www.linkedin.com
- **edX** - https://www.edx.org/
- **Coursera** - https://www.coursera.org/
- **Udemy** - https://www.udemy.com/

"When you learn, teach. When you get, give." - Maya Angelou

Community - It is critical to have your own personal board of directors as well as a community that will support you in your career. Go out there and give back. Join organizations that share your goals and passions. Here are a few corporate-related national organizations that can assist you in networking and skill development.

- **Latinas Rising Up In HR**
  https://www.latinasrisingupinhr.com/
- **Hispanic Association on Corporate Responsibility**
  https://hacr.org/
- **The Association of Latino Professionals for America**
  https://www.alpfa.org/
- **Society of Hispanic Professional Engineers**
  https://shpe.org/

- **Prospanica** - The Association of Hispanic MBAs & Business Professionals - https://www.prospanica.org/
- **United Latinas** - https://www.unitedlatinas.com/
- **The Latinista** - https://www.thelatinista.com/
- **Latinas in Tech** - https://latinasintech.org/
- **Hispanic Technology Executive Council** https://www.hitecglobal.org/
- **HispanicPro** - https://www.hispanicpro.com/
- **National Hispanic Corporate Council** https://www.nhcchq.org/

"I can promise you that women working together, linked, informed, and educated, can bring peace to this forsaken planet."
- Isabel Allende

I truly hope you have enjoyed reading my book. I put a lot of love and positive energy into writing this to reach as many Latinas as possible on their corporate journey. I hope you feel heard, and you know that you are not alone. Remember, you cannot have it all at the same time. Things will change and fluctuate in your family and professional life. What distinguishes us Latinas is that we know how to navigate, overcome, and thrive; all we need to do is believe we can. For change to happen, we must start with ourselves. We also need to start helping each other grow to make an impact. Tell another woman when you admire something she's done. We must make it a habit to lift one another up and not knock each other down. **Be the kind of Latina that supports other Latinas.**

ABOUT THE AUTHOR

Myriam Del Angel has over twenty years of experience as a bilingual human resource professional. She has advised leadership on all aspects of human resources and Diversity, Equity, and Inclusion. She holds a bachelor's degree in human resources from Northeastern Illinois University and has worked for companies such as Arthur Andersen, Microsoft, the University of Chicago, Accenture, Deloitte, E&Y, the University of IL at Chicago, PwC, and Grant Thornton.

Myriam is a contributing author for *Latinas Rising Up in HR Volume 1*, a book that proudly showcases incredible stories of inspiring women making a difference and rising in the HR field across multiple industries. She also participates in panels and podcasts about career development, human resources, and Latina empowerment.

She is a foodie, and loves Latin dancing, CorePower yoga, and traveling. Myriam is Colombian and Mexican and is a proud mom of three teenagers who love and play soccer. She spends her time between Chicago and Miami.

Myriam Del Angel
- **LinkedIn:** mdmiranda
- **Instagram:** myriamhrlatina

Made in the USA
Monee, IL
17 August 2023

41165836R00079